PAGES FROM ANOTHER WORLD

PAGES FROM ANOTHER WORLD

DOMENICO MAZZONE
&
PETER MAZZONE

Pentland Press, Inc.
www.pentlandpressusa.com

PUBLISHED BY PENTLAND PRESS, INC.
5122 Bur Oak Circle, Raleigh, North Carolina 27612
United States of America
919-782-0281

ISBN 1-57197-253-6
Library of Congress Control Number: 00-134893

Printed in the United States of America

To Graziella,

an honest woman,
a devoted wife,
and a
caring mother.

That is why God is God . . .
sublime in all of His creations.
She is the purest of all His works.
Above all malicious things is the divine throb.
Here, the Lord set no limits . . .
and made the beauty more than beauty . . .
as He likes it.
At the end of the work, the power
allowed her to make the species,
according to her pleasure.
What and how does she think,
and what does she say to herself?
And us still there, ignoring
the strength and the value.
She is there, in time and place,
swerves from our Lord's order . . .
I see the time coming
that the Holy Voice says:
Let the confusion of the race
stop. I made and wanted you to make
the species, and to preserve it.
Over the border goes your ambition . . .
and you no longer follow My order.
You and your race must end
by a slowly foretold death.
I will do all over again the beauty race.
But don't say a word . . .
Nobody knows this, just me.

This book is about the fascinating mystery of the multiplication of the human species. Contrary to contemporary thought, the following pages explore the way in which women are the sole determiners of the gender, sexual orientation, and mental and physical stability of their offspring. In being so, they predetermine in each one of us the way we will mature, behave, and function later in life. They are, in fact, in total control of the future evolution of the species.

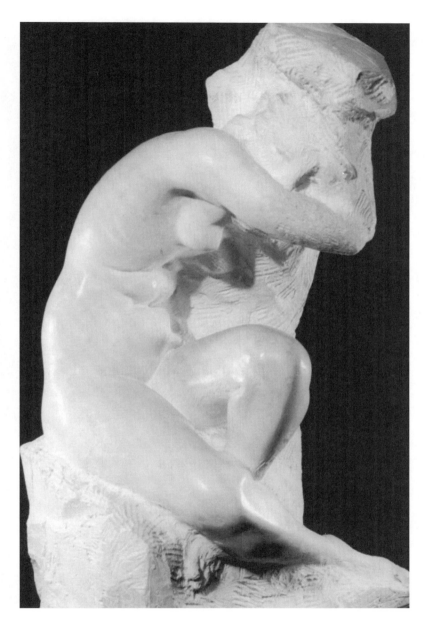

And here she is, that
Because of her . . . allow us,
See the stars, that the
World go around, ... And
So many other things
Good, and bad.

FOREWORD

It was never really my idea to write a book about such a controversial subject. Innocently enough, this all began when a friend of mine said something to me a long time ago that I found to be both offensive and cruel. Ever since that day I found myself thinking about his comments, over and over again, trying to understand if there was some logical explanation for them. I became rather obsessed about the whole thing because my friend's comments led me to feel inferior to many other people within my peer group; and this, more than anything else, gave me the drive and determination to methodically try to figure out whether what he said had any substance to it. From that day forward I began to take personal notes on the subject.

I was certainly aware of the fact that for many people my concerns were unimportant, something not even worth thinking about. For me, however, they became an all-encompassing frustration that consumed the better part of my days back then. I started asking people about the subject—older people, people with much more experience than myself, doctors, anyone that crossed my path that I felt would, or should, know something about the subject matter. All I ever received as feedback, however, seemed to be either nonresponsive babble, incomprehensible medical jargon, or, at best, evasive answers.

In my relentless pursuit to try and figure out my "problem," I found myself many times on the wrong path to understanding it. In fact, what started happening was that I began to think that I must have been cracking up or something. I mean, here I was, a grown man, tormenting myself with something that nobody else cared about, or if they did, they certainly weren't willing to admit that to me.

Around this time I began to pay attention to old proverbs and sayings, old wives tales and the like, not only from my part of the world, but also from various ethnic groups with rich histories and strong traditions. I also started doing research on the various superstitions that many people believe in. And I'm not talking about the relatively benign, one-line superstitions like walking under ladders, or black cats crossing your path and all that. I started concentrating on the very deep-seated superstitions that have driven all kinds of people's lives, like the Ghanian tribes of Africa, the Arabian people of the Middle East, and some of the ancient ethnic groups of Asia and Europe.

Oddly enough, it was these tales, proverbs, and superstitions, incredible though they seem, that provided a catalyst and the necessary starting point to my understanding of my friend's comments. Over time, my thoughts on the subject developed into a firm belief in a theory that offers some catastrophic and alarming conclusions.

From the outset I should point out that my theory had its beginnings in a section of Italy locally known as *Il Meridione*. Generally speaking, this is the portion south of Rome that includes the "heel" and the "toe" of Italy's boot. It includes the provinces of Naples, Bari, Taranto and Reggio di Calabria, to name a few. The people of this region are a down-to-earth, very close-knit group with a rich history and strong traditional values that even today remain virtually unchanged from centuries past.

This region of Italy is the type of place where, even today, most of the people work the land just like the many generations before them. They are a hard-working group that picks olives and grapes from the land and makes oil and wine with their own hands. The kind of people that come home from the fields at night and have a ritual-like dinner on a daily basis with the whole family circle partaking in "God's blessing" around the kitchen table. They have no money, don't do drugs, and have little need for the materialistic things that drive life in western society. Instead, they prefer to gather around with their family at night and get drunk with the same grapes that they squeeze and thank the Lord for providing their meal for another day.

In these regions of Italy, people are spiritual, religious, and, above all, superstitious. To them good luck, bad luck, fortune, and misfortune are all the workings of the almighty Creator. The traditional belief is that things don't happen arbitrarily. On the contrary, there is a reason for everything, and the Lord is the only one that knows the reasons for the successes and tragedies of particular families and individuals. In the Meridione of Italy when strange things happen or unexplainable events occur, it is either a miracle or the wrath of God. And it is not uncommon for an "innocent" individual to pay, by way of a personal tragedy, for something for which his family or ancestors were actually responsible.

In fact, this is exactly how the stories, proverbs, and superstitions begin in this part of the world. If a tragedy befalls a family, for example, the townspeople congregate at the market in the town square, or piazza, on Saturday and recount all of the prior bad acts of some members of the victims' family and conclude that the newest tragedy has somehow evened the score. "Think for yourself, because the Lord thinks for the others," the people will say, knowing that nothing goes unnoticed by the Lord. Similarly, if a crime is committed and the culprit is not caught, the local folks will meet on Sunday on the church steps, talk about the tragedy, and find comfort in the old proverb that says, "Be good and forget; be evil and think." This saying alone will assure them that they need not worry because even if the suspect is never caught, he'll always be trapped in his own mind for what he's done because the Lord will see to it that he's punished in some way. This is what the people believe.

These proverbs and superstitions drive virtually every aspect of life for the people of southern Italy, much more so than they do in Western society. Proverbs and old tales provide explanations for tragedies, crimes, physical handicaps, love, marriage, homosexuality, and just about anything else. For this reason, people are quick to respond to a particular situation with a quick one-liner meant to contain some profound message that has withstood the test of time in this part of the world. And it is precisely this kind of one-liner that my friend relayed to me, that gave rise to the theory that I want to share with you.

Town Square in Rutigliano

1

BEGINNINGS

It all began many years back in the small town of Rutigliano di Bari, a small town in southern Italy. The year was 1948, and I was a young man at that stage in life when all men perceive themselves as carefree, happy-go-lucky individuals. At that time I was twenty-one years old, and my nights were usually spent with a few close friends in front of the town bar looking for available women, and spending the night telling tall tales that all young men tell over a few drinks.

Ever since my youth I have always wanted to become friends with people that I perceived as being better than me. They either had to be richer than me, smarter than me, more educated, or higher up the social ladder in the community than me or my family. I guess the reason for this was because I desperately wanted to transcend the status that my own family occupied back then. My father had died when I was only four years old, which left my mother alone to raise my sister and me. As a result, we were very poor and fatherless to boot, which made my early years extremely difficult. As time went on, my mother married a man who was very strict and abusive, which made my life more miserable than words can describe. By the time I was a teen, not only were we very poor, even by southern Italian standards, but living at home was pure hell. This was the principal reason why I was always attracted to kids that were better than me. When I was with them, my spirits would be lifted and I would forget about all of the problems that existed within my immediate family.

To be perfectly honest, throughout my life I've had very few close friends. That period of my life was no different. Back in those days I was very close with two other guys around my same age. We would hang out together on a daily basis and would usually meet in front of the town bar at night to spend the hours talking about the local gossip because that was the only thing to do in the little town of Rutigliano. Bars in southern Italy are not like bars in America, or at least they weren't back then. They are not the kind of place where people go to get drunk. Rather, they are more like cafés. Even the young people that would hang out there would not be there to get drunk. That doesn't mean that we wouldn't have drinks now and then, but that wasn't the reason to go there. We went because everybody who was anybody would either be at the bar, sitting at sidewalk tables in front of the bar, or, alternatively, gathering on the walkways of the town square, which coincidentally were overlooked by the bar. In short, it was the place to be if young men wanted to be noticed by young women and vice versa.

For simplicity I will refer to my two friends as friend number one, or the rich one, and friend number two, or the poor one. Friend number one, the rich one, was very rich indeed. His father was in the business of producing olive oil from locally grown olives, which are very plentiful in that part of the country. He owned his own company, had many employees working for him, and had amassed a fortune over the years. Friend number two, the poor one, in contrast was really poor. He was a construction worker who spent more time looking for work than actually working. He would get odd-and-end jobs from time to time, followed by long periods of unemployment. As a rule I would try to stay away from his type back in those days, but this guy was so funny that you could not help but want to hang around with him. You could be assured that if he was around, the time spent would be fun and entertaining. With these two friends I felt very comfortable. The rich one made me feel as if I was rich myself, and, therefore, that gave me the opportunity to hang around with his friends; and the poor one would keep me laughing all the time, making it easy for me to stay away from my stepfather and forget about my problems. Our friendship lasted for many years, spanning virtually all of my youth and young adulthood.

Certainly every beginning has an ending, and this friendship was no exception. When we were least expecting it, my rich friend surprised us in the bar one night by telling us that he had proposed to the girl he loved and she had accepted his hand in marriage. My poor friend and I were happy for him and we celebrated the night away, but we both felt bittersweet about the whole thing because we knew that from this point on our rich friend would no longer be able to spend as much time with us and we would be left on our own. Two poor nobodies, fending for themselves. And this in fact is what happened. After that night, we all said our good-byes, all the while thinking that from now on it would only be the two of us, me and my poor friend, the want-to-be comedian, that would have to fend for ourselves.

Surprisingly, our habits didn't change all that much, and me and the comedian would still meet in front of the bar on an almost nightly basis. Our rich friend would also come around once in a while, and although it wasn't like before, we still kept a strong friendship with him. Time passed, and it wasn't long until one night while we sat at the bar our rich friend came by and told us that he was going to be a father. We were so happy for him and, even though both my poor friend and I felt a bit of envy, we celebrated the night away and comforted ourselves by saying that it wouldn't be long until our time would come to enjoy the gifts of marriage and fatherhood.

Sure enough, a short time later my poor friend also told me that he would be getting married soon to the girl he had met some time earlier. He couldn't wait to be with her and become a father just like our rich friend. Naturally we all got together at the bar and celebrated this event and spent the night singing and dancing and smoking cigars. Both of my friends were really happy. You could see it in their eyes, and I was happy for them too; but inside I felt a bit lonely, depressed, and envious because I now felt like I would be all alone for eternity.

So there I found myself, the only remaining bachelor out of the trio. The nightly meetings at the bar stopped, friend number two got married, and I found myself all alone with no one to spend my time with. Luckily, both of my friends had married local women and made their home in town, for that is the way it is in southern Italy and, therefore, we still managed to get together once in a while at the bar. My rich friend's wife had given birth to a beautiful baby boy. Sometimes when he came around he would bring his boy with him for all to see. In the meantime, my poor friend was awaiting his turn at becoming a father, and he also informed us one night that his wife was now expecting a child as well.

More time passed. I started concentrating on settling down myself because the age of dreams had come and gone, and I was becoming very unhappy in my solitude. I was having a hard time of it, however, mainly due to my family's low social status and lack of finances. I did not appeal to the families of the available single women; and back in those days in that part of the world, it wasn't just the girl that had to be interested, but her family as well. Even though my poor friend had managed to find a girl and a family that would have him, I was having a much tougher time of it. Right around this time my poor friend became a father. His wife had given birth to a beautiful baby girl. Once again the three of us went through the ritual at the bar, celebrating the good fortune of the poor one, and all the while I kept noticing how the time passed while I remained single. It wasn't long before my two friends each had another child, the rich one another baby boy, and the poor one another girl. We celebrated again. More time went by as my misery continued.

Shortly thereafter, and quite by accident, I found a woman for myself. My family's history and financial status meant I could not even hope for her family's approval because she came from a rich background. Her father was an undertaker who had built a monopoly in a nearby town. Her brother was a banker in Bari, the big city around those parts, and her whole family was well known in the local area. She knew that her family would never approve of us being together because I was a peasant from a very poor family, but she loved me nonetheless. I also knew that for me this was the chance of a lifetime to escape my miserable situation at home, which was becoming worse all the time. Not wanting such a beautiful woman to slip away from me, I asked her to elope with me. Surprisingly she agreed. We ran away in the middle of one summer night in June of 1954 and got married.

Unlike my friends, I didn't have a big party and didn't get the chance to celebrate at the bar with my friends because of the circumstances, but that didn't bother me at all, because at last I was married to a truly beautiful woman. In addition, I immediately felt happier because I knew that I would be able to escape my miserable situation at home. After several months went by, my wife and I returned to my hometown of Rutigliano, and eventually both of us got together with my friends and their respective families at the bar for coffee, drinks, and conversation. Things were different now, of course, because we all had responsibilities to worry about and other things on our mind. In this sense our meetings were not like they used to be, but because we were loyal old friends, we felt free to discuss even the most intimate details of our married life.

In southern Italy, the predominant faith is Christian, and virtually everyone is Roman Catholic. Every year in the month of September, the Catholic church celebrates Christ, and the whole region joins in. There are processions and parades, open markets, and singing and dancing in all the town squares of the region. The local bakeries deliver their best pastries to the various restaurants, cafés, and bars while the people take their seats in front of these establishments and watch the festivities around them. There are vendors, bands, performers, and various religious shows going on all at once. In short, a good time is had by all during this time of the year.

In 1958 during this annual "Feast of the Crucifix," as it is called, my two friends and I took our respective seats at a table in front of the bar and were enjoying ourselves watching the parade passing by. All of us had our wives and kids with us, and by this time my rich friend had three boys, my poor friend had three girls, and I had two girls. We were laughing and joking, exchanging compliments about our children, saying things like "Oh, yours are the cutest," "No, his are the cutest," "Mine are the cutest" and so on until the conversation focused on baby girls and baby boys. We started discussing the fact that both me and my poor friend had daughters, while my rich friend had sons. The discussion turned into a small argument as to the reasons why this might be. It was during this occasion that my rich friend made a most disturbing comment, and even though he said it in a relatively happy tone without any malice at all, it was a disturbing comment nonetheless. "I can have sons," he said to my friend and me, "but you two could never even hope to have any. You will always have girls because you are incapable of producing boys."

As soon as he made that comment, our table became silent. Nobody said a word. Both my poor friend and I looked at each other in a kind of stupor, wanting but not able to say anything, while our respective wives looked at each other, then down at the table without saying a word. In the meantime, the rich friend's wife just looked at all of us and smiled, assuming the attitude of a sort of superwoman. It was friend number two, the comedian, that finally managed to break the silence, but by that time the damage had been done. The words had such a profound effect on all of us that night that we were not able to enjoy the rest of the evening. From that night on I felt as if friend number one, the rich one, had never really been my friend at all. I stopped getting together with him completely. It was as if his comments had brought an abrupt end to a long and sincere friendship. It's hard to describe in words how that phrase made me feel. I kept repeating it in my head over and over again. I felt humiliated and insecure every time I did so. There were two things, aside from his actual words, that really hurt me deeply. The first was that he had said them in front of my wife, and the second was the reaction that his own wife had when he said it. It was as if she had taken on the attitude of a proud peacock, almost as if to show that she was better than the other two women, and that her husband was better than us. It made me feel like I just didn't rate as a man.

For a long period of time I kept repeating that phrase to myself over and over again. I would ask myself why it was that he had male children and I didn't. I actually started thinking that he might be right after all. That is, I started believing that for some reason I was just incapable of producing male offspring. Was it because I was lacking something that he had? Could it be that he was just a superior human being? This didn't really make sense to me because I felt that despite his money, I was just as good as him, if not better than him. So why was it that my rich friend had three boys and I still didn't have any after two tries? And, for that matter, why was it that my friend the comedian had also not produced any boys?

I started thinking that perhaps I was abnormal in some way, but I just couldn't accept that. After all, I had managed, with my wife's help at least, to produce two gorgeous and healthy little girls that everybody adored. I also felt healthy myself, both in

"You are incapable of producing boys."

mind and body, so it was difficult for me to believe that my inability to have boys could have anything to do with any physical or medical problem on my part. It was for this reason that I started thinking to myself that maybe it had nothing to do with me at all. Maybe it had something to do with my wife. Or maybe it had something to do with my rich friend's wife, or my comedian friend's wife.

I knew both my friends' wives very well. We had spent lots of time together at each other's house for dinner, nights out on the town, visiting, and so on. For this reason I had come to know both of them very well on a personal level. As I started thinking about them, the kind of women they were and the kind of men they had attracted, a composite picture of the two couples became embedded in my mind. My rich friend had married a woman who not only came from a poor family but was also the kind of woman that few would consider attractive. On the other hand, my poor friend had married a woman who came from a very wealthy family and was also good looking. I then compared their respective situations with my own and couldn't help but feel that I had been very lucky indeed. Despite my miserable youth and my poor upbringing, I had managed to marry one of the most beautiful women in the local area. And I don't say this because she happened to be my wife. I mean she was truly gorgeous. In addition, she came from one of the wealthiest families around that was well respected from everyone in the community. Indeed, even to this day I still don't know why she became attracted to me; but the fact is that she did, and for all I could tell she seemed to be truly in love with me. This really did something for my self-esteem. I felt as if I was the most fortunate man on the face of the earth.

With these composite sketches in mind, I started focusing on other things about our respective relationships as I tried to decipher whether my friend's words had any substance to them. I started remembering all of the conversations that my friends and I had over the years while we sat in front of the bar, paying specific attention to details about the dynamics of our lives and our problems in the context of our relationships with our wives. I started remembering the things that were important to my rich friend. He had always been the king in his house, so to speak. He gave all the orders, he made all the decisions, he paid all the bills, he would determine if, and when, the family would go out. In short, he was in total control at home. His wife's role in his house was simply to make sure that he was always taken care of, that the kids were well kept, that the household chores were all done, and that was it. Everything he said or asked for was essentially an order for his wife, and she had better obey him or else. She in turn did everything for him and then some, to the point that we (my other friend and I) would become sick to our stomachs just witnessing his treatment of her.

For my poor friend, on the other hand, it was a totally different ball game. Just listening to his situation at home could bring sadness and tears to my eyes. In his house his wife ruled. Not only did she make all the decisions, but she insisted that he cater to her every need. Every Sunday he would have to take her to his in-laws for the day, but she would never go with him to her in-laws. He was obligated to buy her every little thing she wanted, but if he ever wanted anything she would object and complain that there simply wasn't enough money to go around. When they went out it was always on her terms; and if she didn't want to go, then that meant that he couldn't go either. Because he was one of the nicest people that one could ever meet, he never objected to any of this. In order to keep the peace, he would forsake everything for her, never raised his voice to her, and always obeyed her every command.

The contrast, at least in my own mind, was clear as a bell. In my rich friend's house everything had to be done the way he wanted it, whereas in my poor friend's house everything had to be done the way his wife wanted it. It was obvious that these two families had evolved in two opposite directions. And it was also obvious that in the first situation the result had been three boys, while the second situation had produced three girls. All of this was nice, I said to myself as I thought about my problem, but it hadn't gotten me any closer to understanding anything. Indeed, it hadn't gotten me anywhere, but I kept thinking as I started reflecting on my own family and the dynamics in my own home. It seemed to me that my own situation was almost identical to my poor friend's. After all, my wife was always putting me down for one reason or another. We weren't rich, and I couldn't compete with the standard of living that she had been used to at home. She resented me for that. My family was neither well educated nor well respected like her family, and she disliked that as well. In addition, having run away with me, she had distanced herself from her family and friends, and now found herself living in another town where she was obliged to deal with people that she felt were of a lower class than she was used to. She would complain about that. Consequently, she would always insist on spending time with her family, getting out of my "redneck" town, wanting lots of material things to make her feel like she did before she left home, telling me what I should do and how I should do it to improve the family situation, et cetera, et cetera.

The more I tried to analyze and understand my friend's comment, the more I came upon dead ends, probably because I hadn't even realized what it was that I was trying to find out or what it was that I was trying to understand. After a considerable amount of thinking on the subject, I reached the following conclusions:

1. For his wife, my rich friend was everything, while ، for my wife and my poor friend's wife we were basically worthless nobodies.

2. The comedian and I were dirt poor and our friend was very rich.

3. My rich friend's wife was relatively ugly, my poor friend's wife was attractive, and my wife was beautiful.

4. My rich friend had three boys, my poor friend had three girls, and I had two girls.

I started thinking that maybe, just maybe, my friend's comment about the two of us not being able to produce boys might have something to do with the fact that we were poor and he was rich. This seemed to make little sense to me, but with my limited understanding, it seemed to be the only common denominator.

Searching for an answer in those days was not easy for me. It wasn't as if I could go to the local library to do some scholarly work and come up with an answer. We're talking about the small

"I didn't know whether there was an answer."

town of Rutigliano in southern Italy in the late 1950s. But more importantly, I should note that even if a library was available, I wouldn't know what to do anyway, because I had never done any research.

One thing was for sure, whatever it was that I was trying to understand was really eating away at me. I wanted to know why it was that I had not had any boys and whether or not it was true that I was incapable, as my friend had told me, of producing any. I didn't know how it was that I was going to get to the bottom of my problem, but I now realized that it was no longer a problem, but rather an obsession. What made the whole thing unbearable was that I didn't know whether there was an answer, or if there was, what I had to do to search for it.

After that infamous night at the bar I didn't really have any close friends. I still went to the bar once in a while, but all the people I knew there could better be categorized as acquaintances. One night while I was sitting in front of the bar, one such acquaintance came over to me and began telling me that he had noticed a change in me lately and asked if everything was all right. I assured him that I felt fine physically and otherwise. But he insisted that maybe I should go see a doctor. "You're just not the same, Domenico," he said. "Maybe you should go see a doctor. Sometimes if something's wrong with you the first sign of trouble are your spirits. And I have to admit, you seem so down lately," he said. "I just think it would do you a world of good if you just went to see somebody. At least they'll be able to tell you if there's anything that you should worry about, and if everything checks out, that alone will lift your spirits."

I decided to follow my friend's advice and made an appointment to see an old friend of the family who had become a doctor. As I went there I asked myself what the doctor would think. After all, I felt fine physically and didn't really have a complaint as far as my health was concerned. But then I started thinking that since he was a doctor, perhaps he could shed some light on the questions I had concerning my problem. Certainly, I thought, doctors should know these things. They were required to go through extensive schooling and probably had studied all about the subject of sex determination and what was responsible for it and so on. I figured that I would go there with the excuse of getting a routine check-up and then simply ask the doctor what he knew about this whole subject matter. He might think that I was naive in even asking such a question, but he and I were pretty good friends. He knew that I had no formal education, so I figured that at the very least he would understand and just answer my question. At the very least I thought he could point me in the right direction so that I could go and read up on the whole reproduction issue on my own. I decided that this was a great idea, and off I went.

When I got to his office we greeted each other and exchanged a few words about our families. Then he asked me why I had come to see him. "Are you feeling all right, Domenico, or is something wrong?"

"Well, Doc, I decided that I better come in for a check-up. It's not that I feel physically ill or anything, but for some time now I've been feeling kind of strange, so I decided to come in," I said. "You know I've never even had a regular check-up and I thought it would make me feel better if I could get a clean bill of health from you," I said.

"All right, Domenico," he responded and proceeded to give me a complete check-up. When he was finished he told me that I was as healthy as an ox for all he could tell. At least physically. "You have absolutely nothing to worry about," he exclaimed. "But what about everything else? Is everything all right at home with the wife and the kids?"

"Oh, everything is fine with them, Doc, thank God for that," I said.

"So what's the real reason for your coming here?" he asked.

"Well to be honest, Doc, I did really want to make sure that I was in good health, but to tell you the truth there is also another reason why I came here," I said. "Something has been bugging me for quite some time, and I'd like to ask you some questions about the subject to kind of put my mind at ease."

"Of course, Domenico," he exclaimed. "Tell me, what's on your mind?" he asked, somewhat surprised.

I proceeded to tell him the whole story about what my friend had said, the fact that I had two girls and wanted a boy, the fact that he had three boys, et cetera. I ended my part of the conversation by asking him whether or not there could be any medical reasons for my inability to produce male offspring. After

"All right, Domenico," he responded, and proceeded to give me a complete checkup.

listening to me he shook his head and gave me a sarcastic smile. "You know, Domenico, I'd like to know the same thing. One would think that I should know the answer to those kinds of questions, being a doctor and all. Fact is that I have two girls myself and also want a son to carry the family name, but for some reason I haven't been able to have one yet either. Scientifically," he continued, "the sex of a child is determined by whether or not the male contributes the Y chromosome or the X chromosome to the female egg through his sperm." He then proceeded to go into a long discussion that was totally incomprehensible to me. He spoke about chromosomes, hormones, white blood cells, red blood cells, and all sorts of other things that I didn't understand. As he spoke I found myself listening to what sounded like a totally foreign language, although I'm sure he was trying to make it as elementary as possible. Finally he concluded by telling me that even though scientific research had been progressing by leaps and bounds, this was one area that was still not well understood. "Perhaps in the future, as science advances, we will know more," he said, "but I think that it's the woman who determines whether her children will be little girls or little boys. The woman does as she pleases, and all we can do is sit there and wait to see what it is that she will produce." He continued. "Right now people in the medical circles are saying that that's probably not what happens. The medical research suggests that it may be the male that actually has the most to do with the sex of the child, but I believe the opposite is true. That's all I can tell you, Mazzone," he added.

On my way home I started thinking about what the doctor had told me. I felt that without knowing it he had put me on the right path to understanding my problem. To me it was a foregone conclusion that I would never be able to understand all of the medical mumbo-jumbo that he had told me about. That didn't make me feel too bad, however, because even the doctor had told me that the medical and scientific research were inconclusive on the subject. As I walked I started thinking about what the doctor had told me about his desire for a boy, and I started thinking about the woman he had married. She was a real beauty, the type of woman that every man would be grateful to have at his side. And she was rich, too. She came from one of the wealthiest and most noble families in town. It also occurred to me, however, that the doctor was not a slouch either. He also came from a well respected family that was pretty well off financially. Yet he had not been able to produce a son. This was significant to me because it undermined my initial conclusions about the subject. Certainly if being poor had anything to do with sex determination, then the doctor's situation was partly inconsistent with that. He should have been able to produce boys, I thought to myself, because he was not poor. True, he wasn't as rich as his wife, but wouldn't that mean that there should be a split regarding the sex of the children in his family? Yet there he was, with two children already and both of them were girls. I started feeling really stupid for even having thought that money or wealth could have anything to do with it, but something inside told me that although that might not be the total answer, I could not simply discard the financial issue completely. I would have to keep it on the back burner as a possible, but not exclusive, factor.

I decided that I would begin to take note of the families that I knew and see if my rich-versus-poor idea had any validity. I started asking friends about their family situation—subtly, of course—with the objective of testing my hypothesis. I inquired about my friends' families, their wives' families, how many children they had, how many were boys and how many were girls, et cetera. As time went on, I expanded my inquiries to acquaintances and people I didn't even know. I just acted as if I was sincerely concerned about them. At the same time, to make them feel more at ease with my questions, I would comment on my own roots and my family, my wife's family, my two girls, and so on.

As the results came in, I felt that I might actually be on to something. It seemed to me that the family and financial status of the bride and groom's respective backgrounds was certainly a factor that had to be taken into account when it came to predicting the sex of their children. The problem was that the results were not very clear cut, and the whole thing could very well be due to coincidence. There were so many close calls that I could not really be sure. For example, some couples with very similar backgrounds had boys whereas other couples from really different financial backgrounds had children of both sexes. Moreover, there were many different circumstances and situations that just didn't fit nicely into my theory. I had no explanation for these apparent aberrations and decided that there must be something else going on, perhaps in addition to family background and wealth.

As I continued tabulating my results, something else happened that changed the direction of my thinking and made me realize that, indeed, there were other factors that I had to take into account. As I mentioned earlier, southern Italy, and particularly the region where I grew up, is made up of very superstitious people. Almost everyone adheres to closely held beliefs and old wives' tales that have been repeated through many generations. One such tale, germane to this writing, concerns pregnant women. It turns out that many people in this part of the world believe that when women are pregnant they spontaneously desire certain things. It may be, for example, that for whatever reason, or for no reason at all, a pregnant woman may feel like having pizza, or pickles and milk, pasta and cheese, and so on at a particular time of day. I've even heard of people in America believing in this kind of thing. The difference is that in Italy these beliefs are much more pervasive and rigidly held. For example, many people there believe that unless these "unusual" or "spontaneous" desires of pregnant women are immediately satisfied, their offspring may suffer serious consequences. Unlike Americans, the people in Italy are of the opinion that if a pregnant woman does have a random wish or spontaneous desire, the man must do everything in his power to provide the woman with whatever it is that she wants. The reason is that if he doesn't, then the unfulfilled desire will manifest itself as a birthmark or, worse yet, a scar on the pregnant woman's future child. In some cases, such birthmarks may be totally inconspicuous and inoffensive, but in other cases they may be very obvious indeed, and may also cause physical or mental defects in the offspring. It turns out that most people in America neither believe nor appreciate this phenomenon, but in southern Italy not only do people believe it, they live by it.

Back in 1958 I knew about these local superstitions, but, like many others, I dismissed them as meaningless and unsubstantiated fables until one night when I ran into an old acquaintance of mine while I was sitting in the famous bar tabulating my results. We struck up a conversation. While the two of us were talking, a young girl walked into the bar with her mother. "Don't you know who that is?" he said. "That's so-and-so's wife and her daughter." As I looked up I saw a little girl standing at the counter with her mother and noticed that I had seen them around town before. It was impossible to miss the small girl. She was a very cute child who looked just like her mother, but she had a very large, distinct birthmark on the left side of her face. As I turned around to look at her, she turned in my direction and yelled to her father who was sitting at a table behind us. In the artificial light of the bar the birthmark was very obvious. It looked like a large, light brown stain on her face, extending from just below her right jaw all the way up to her upper cheek just below her right eye. It looked as if somebody had just thrown a cup of coffee in her face and she hadn't cleaned it off yet. It made you want to go right up to her and wipe it off. As I looked back toward the person she was yelling to, I noticed that I had seen her father before and decided to go up to him and ask how it was that she got that mark on her face.

"When her mother was pregnant," he explained, "she would always want to go and visit friends and have fun. I would always take her wherever she wanted to go, and one day we ended up having dinner with some friends of ours. While we were there, the people next door had made some coffee, and the smell spread to our friends' house. My wife asked our friends to make some coffee, but they were out. My wife kept telling me that she really felt like having some coffee, so I decided to go to the store to get some. Unfortunately, when I got there, the store was closed so I came back empty-handed. I apologized to my wife, and she told me not to worry. She just rested her face in her hand and told me that she didn't feel like having coffee anymore anyway. I never thought about it again until our daughter was born with that mark on her face. I mean, the stain on her face looks so much like a coffee stain to me that every time I look at her I wonder if she would not have that mark on her face had I been able to get some coffee for my wife that night. I know this sounds weird and everything, but it makes me think that the old timers may be right when they speak of pregnant women and how they have to get their wishes fulfilled and all," he explained.

This was the first time that I had heard an actual story purporting to document the old superstition that I had heard

"I never thought about it again until our daughter was born with a mark on her face."

many times before about pregnant women. I didn't want to believe that these old tales had any merit to them but that little girl's face had made such an impression on me that I started to think twice about it. How can it possibly be that just by putting her hand to her face she could have made that mark on her own daughter? I thought to myself. As I ended the conversation with the girl's father, I stored the thought away, left the bar, and headed home.

Since that day I've come across and documented so many stories like the one I just described that I could fill a volume with them alone. For the purposes of this book, however, I'll relate just one more that I happened to come across just recently which impressed me tremendously. It happened one day when a friend of mine came to visit me at my studio. He is a retired policeman who has taken an interest in sculpture now that he has lots of free time on his hands. Knowing that I've been a sculptor for many years, he started coming to my studio asking me if I would help him get started on his new hobby. He started showing up once or twice a week to try his hand at sculpting and we would often wind up talking about everything under the sun. On this particular day a few years back, I started telling him about the book that I was writing, explained that one of the early chapters in the book dealt with the issue of birthmarks and unusual pregnancies, and began to explain to him my thoughts on the subject. As I kept talking, I noticed that he became very silent and quietly started crying. Not knowing what had sparked this emotion in him, I asked whether I had upset him. He told me the following unbelievable story.

He was supposed to have been the youngest of three brothers, but the second child died shortly after his birth due to very unfortunate circumstances. It turns out that when his mother was pregnant with her second child, the family had gone on a little vacation to a well known amusement park in New Jersey. While there they went to the arcade and started playing some of the games. Eventually they stopped at a glass case that contained lots of different prizes. The case was equipped with mechanical hooks that moved freely about the enclosed compartment and could be lowered down towards the prizes. For a quarter, a person could move the hooks directly above the desired object and then, by pushing a button, the hooks lowered, opened, and tried to grab a prize. If successful, the hooks could then be maneuvered back to the front of the case to deposit the prize in a slot where the operator could retrieve it. If unsuccessful, the operator would have to insert another quarter to once again activate the hooks. Among the many available prizes there happened to be a stuffed monkey that the policeman's mother really liked. She asked her husband to try and get it for her, but even though he tried many different times and hooked several prizes, he couldn't get the monkey. Finally, after spending lots of money and becoming really angry and frustrated over the whole thing, the husband told his wife that he had no more money and he was done trying for the monkey. Frustrated and sad, they made their way out of the arcade and went home.

"Believe it or not," the policeman said, "nine months later my mother gave birth to a baby that resembled a monkey more than a human. He was born with a weird medical condition that the doctors could not explain. The baby was very hairy, sickly, and died shortly thereafter when the doctors pulled the plug on him," he said. As he told me this story, I could see that the memories still had a profound effect on this man, even though many years had passed. He concluded his story by telling me that his father had often wondered whether that failed attempt at the toy monkey in the amusement park that day had anything to do with his mother's tragic pregnancy. Then he proceeded to tell me that the whole story was too emotional for him, and we quickly changed subjects.

Over the years I have heard many such stories, some of which are truly incredible, but back in the late fifties when I was concentrating on my boys-versus-girls problem, I had only witnessed a few, the first of which concerned the little girl with the coffee-stain birthmark on her face. She made a big impression on me, and I wondered whether her father's story could be an explanation for her birthmark, or, alternatively, whether the whole thing was a mere coincidence. Could it be that a mother could create such a child by merely touching her face while desiring something she couldn't have during her pregnancy? Did pregnant women have a certain type of power or what-have-you to produce such peculiarities in their offspring? Was it something that they could do purposely, or was

"Believe it or not," the policeman said, "nine months later my mother gave birth to a baby that resembled a monkey more than a human."

it something that they had no control over? I kept going over and over these silly concepts in my mind. It seemed to me that women could not be doing this on purpose, How was it possible that any mother would want anything other than a perfect child? So if it wasn't their doing, what force could be responsible for such horrific results? And if it was true that they could consciously or subconsciously produce such peculiarities by merely desiring certain things, did they also have the power to control and manipulate the sex of their children? Their offspring's sexual preferences? their personality traits? The whole concept to me was troublesome, intriguing and inexplicable, all at the same time. I wanted nothing more than to understand it and explore all of the possible avenues in an attempt to find an answer.

Whenever I brought up the subject with other people, almost all of them would laugh at me and my weird fascination with the subject. Invariably all of them would say that such occurrences were the result of God's will and that the mothers (and the fathers, for that matter) had absolutely nothing to do with it. This was not easy for me to accept, because I couldn't believe that God could ever wish birth defects and the like on anybody. Nonetheless, the local townspeople adhered to the strongly held belief that in many cases, such birth defects, birthmarks, et cetera, were simply the Lord's way of evening the score, so to speak, for certain wrongs that the people in question had to pay for in the eyes of God.

As I discovered more and more of these cases, I became even more determined to figure out the driving force behind these phenomena. I also wondered what the parents of these children felt like when they gave birth to imperfect children, retarded children, children born with severe physical and emotional handicaps, children born with strange marks on their extremities, or, worse yet, children that came out of their mothers' wombs as complete monsters. Did this make the mothers feel inadequate?

What about the fathers? Did it make them feel guilty, or perhaps did they feel like horrible human beings themselves for producing such children? I wanted to ask some of these unfortunate parents all of these questions, but I felt ashamed and embarrassed to do so. I was afraid of what their reaction to such questions might be. Perhaps they would be very offended, or worse yet, they might react in a violent kind of way. I just couldn't get up the nerve to go up to anyone and launch into a discussion on this topic.

Even though I had started out thinking that these kinds of superstitions were largely the product of ignorant people, the more I researched the subject and the more cases I discovered, the more I started taking the subject more seriously. By this time my "theory" had evolved to the point that I felt pretty certain that this whole issue of the gender of children was related in some way to the physical and mental well-being of the child at birth. These two things were in some way controlled by some power or force that I could not yet explain. It seemed to me that the mothers of these children were partially, if not totally, responsible for their gender and their condition at birth. Despite my conversation with the doctor, I suspected that the fathers of these children, together with the whole chromosome and hormonal explanations that the doctor so patiently shared with me, had absolutely nothing to do with it. I started convincing myself that there must be some power exclusive to women that gave rise to these things, whether they knew about it or not. The only remaining problem was to figure out what the nature of this force was, where it came from, how it worked, and why it was exclusive to women.

I decided to visit my friend the doctor once again, mainly because I wanted to bounce some of my ideas off of him and ask him a few more questions which I felt he could answer for me. I recalled that the last time I was there he seemed to be interested in my obsession, and he hadn't laughed me out of his office, so I felt that at the very least he didn't think that my ideas were totally ridiculous. When I walked into his office, I saw that he had just finished up with a woman patient that I recognized as a local midwife. Midwives were very common back in those days in southern Italy. In fact, most families hired midwives to help with childbirth just as I had done for my two daughters. It was only in extreme situations that a doctor would become involved. Otherwise families had their children in their home with the help of other women that did that kind of thing for a living. In any case, as I walked in they greeted me and told me that they had just been talking about me and my ideas about children and so on.

"You know, the doctor was telling me about the conversation he had with you the last time you were here," the midwife said. "He was asking me what I thought about the whole thing. I was just explaining to him that I have helped birth hundreds of children, and I have some ideas of my own on the subject."

This was exactly the person I should be talking to about this, I thought to myself. Who would know better than her about this type of thing? Not only is she a woman, but she's also been there when countless women have given birth. Undoubtedly some of them must have shared some very intimate details about their pregnancies, the problems associated with them, the kinds of things that had gone through their minds during the previous nine months, et cetera. I decided to take this opportunity, in the comfort of the doctor's office, to get some answers directly from her in the hope that they might help me understand some of the things I had questions about. Needless to say, we launched into a discussion on the subject right at that moment in the doctor's office.

The first thing I asked the midwife about was what she thought of the mentally-draining types of deliveries, that is, those cases where children were born with severe defects and handicaps. "I've seen many of those in my career," she started. "I remember one case that happened a long time ago right about the time I first started doing this. It was truly depressing and scary for me. This girl, Maria, was twenty-five years old, and she had asked for my assistance during labor. There I was, delivering this newborn, when I saw that as his legs came out they were badly deformed. I mean, they didn't look like a baby's legs should look. They were so scrawny looking to me that they looked more like the legs of a little dog or cat than those of a baby. Even the child's feet looked more like paws than actual feet. The only people in the room were me and Maria and her husband. As soon as I pulled the kid out and showed it to her, she cried out in despair. I thought she was going to die or something. It was a really bad scene. Her husband started crying and screaming. I didn't know what to do, but I knew that something had to be done. When they calmed down and stopped crying hours later, they decided that they were going to

The midwife

kill the child because that would be the best thing to do. They could not bear the thought of raising a child that resembled some kind of animal more than a human being. They begged me to keep the whole thing a secret and just pretend that the baby had been stillborn. Seeing them in so much pain I gave them my word that I would never reveal their secret to anyone, and I haven't to this day. The three of us were the only ones that knew about this terrible tragedy that happened in their life, and we remained friends for years.

"Some time later," she continued, "that young lady told me that during her pregnancy she had been terribly attracted to some dog that a friend of hers had. She tried to get one for herself just like her friend's, but try as they did, they could never find a dog quite like that one. She told me that she used to think about that dog all the time while she was pregnant. She would even go to her friend's house and take the dog out for walks and everything. She was just crazy about that dog. Well, when she explained the story to me, she was still very upset because not only did she still ache for her lost child, but she was also convinced that she had actually caused the child to be born the way he was. After she told me that I couldn't help but think how much the boy had actually resembled a dog when he was born, and we both just looked at each other as she started crying. I stayed there for a while and tried to comfort her until her husband came home. Of course, he thought that she was crying about the same old thing, but I knew the real reason. It depressed me so much. These are things that men do not understand because they cannot understand them. To understand these things, you have to be a woman," she cried.

I decided to go ahead and ask the burning question, just to see what she had to say about it. "Can you tell me," I started, "why it is that both the doctor and I have two girls, even though we both desperately want a boy?" I said.

"I really don't know the answer to that," she replied. "But I can tell you that everyone would like to know the answer to that question. Everybody has a personal opinion about that, but all I can tell you is what I have learned through my experience in this line of business. After a lifetime of delivering babies," she continued, "and sharing intimate conversations with the mothers of those children, I'm convinced that most men are fools. Men only think about a woman's body and how she looks when he's out with her. That's the only thing that matters to them. Most men could care less about the inner feelings of a woman. This is really a problem because women put these things first. We know what men want and the things they'll say to get what they want, even before they think of it. I hope you can read between the lines here, but just in case you can't, the bottom line is that you men don't understand anything. When it comes to a woman's sentiment and a woman's philosophical outlook on life, you guys just don't know anything. The difference between a man and a woman, both physically and mentally, is enormous. You have absolutely no idea how vast it really is. You are, and will always remain, men to us. You understand nothing about what makes us tick. Whether you want to talk about everyday problems, anxieties, objectives in life, painful moments, moments of ecstasy, the important things in life like sacrifices, love, admiration, respect, and honesty, all these things mean one thing for women, and an altogether different thing for men. There is an unimaginable world of difference between the perspectives that women and men have with regard to these things. I'll give you an example," she added as the doctor and I listened like two young students listening to a seasoned professor.

"Have you ever seen the way that a rooster makes love?" she asked. "Next time you witness this, pay close attention to the chicken. I can tell you that if a woman—any woman—is devoted to her man, any man, completely with her body and soul, her mind, sentiments, and emotions, that man will be blessed with baby boys nine times out often. In other words, if a woman reacts to her man the same way a chicken reacts to a rooster, lovemaking will result in male children. On the other hand," she continued, "have you ever watched an eagle as she snares a fish right out of the water? In a second she has an uncanny ability to grip the fish in her beak and quickly fly away. If you've ever seen this, it is truly a remarkable sight. Well, if you can imagine that eagle as representing a woman and that fish as representing a man in a relationship, I can tell you that nine times out of ten he will be the proud father of a baby girl," she exclaimed. "What I'm telling you is based on personal experience, not doctrine. You can choose to believe it or disbelieve it, but If you really don't

The chicken

The eagle

believe it, look around for yourself. Examine the relationship of various couples, and when you're done, I'm sure you'll come around to my way of thinking," she concluded.

The doctor and I looked at each other and remained silent for some time. Finally the midwife opened her purse, took out a sheet of paper, and handed it to me. "Take this," she said as she handed me the paper. "It's a gift from me to you. Study that paper and I wish you good luck in your wish for a boy. Maybe the next one will be just that," she said as she greeted us both and walked out the door. When I got home I looked at the sheet of paper she had given me and studied it for hours and hours. This is what it said:

The Attributes of a Woman

1. *For a woman, a man is the best toy.*

2. *In intimate and tender situations, the woman is always in command.*

3. *When she doesn't want to participate, she says she's not feeling well.*

4. *She can give you so much happiness, but at a very dear price.*

5. *Don't believe a woman who cries. Rarely are the tears real.*

6. *When you see her sleeping, don't always believe she's sleeping.*

7. *The amount of joy she gives you is equal to the amount of pain she gives you.*

8. *For a woman that a man desires, he'll commit the absurd.*

9. *She'll make you believe one thing while she's actually thinking another.*

10. *Her husband's love is never sufficient.*

11. *Sometimes you can make her happy with just one flower.*

12. *All of the great masterpieces were created for women's liking.*

13. *A woman is very happy when you don't blame her for whatever may have gone wrong.*

14. *The number of people killed over women are countless.*

"Sometimes you can make her happy with just one flower."

15. *Women are the perfect beings for making up excuses and fabricating stories.*

16. *For every one she does, she thinks a hundred.*

17. *Where love is concerned, a woman enjoys watching a man suffer.*

18. *She knows how to convince you and make you do the things you don't want to do.*

19. *Giving herself up is her weapon for seduction.*

20. *In time of lovemaking a man is just a boy for a woman.*

21. *The greatest joy of any normal woman is that of being a mother.*

22. *Most women know what men will say before they say it.*

After reading and studying these phrases, I reflected on them for several days; and as I kept analyzing them over and over, some things became clear to me. First, I realized that although I was already married and the father of two children, I understood next to nothing about life in general. Second, it occurred to me that particularly with respect to women, I knew absolutely nothing. To me women were a total, albeit very fascinating, mystery. A mystery that I wanted to solve and understand in every detail once and for all. Perhaps then and only then, I thought to myself, could I even hope to find the answer to the specific question I had about what it is that determines whether or not some women produce males while others produce females.

I decided that this lady was very wise indeed. If I was going to try and figure out anything, I had to start by understanding all of these peculiarities that, according to the midwife, were unique to women. In order to do this, I had to have patience, observe women in painstaking detail, take mental notes of their habits, document everything through written notes to myself, and research everything I possibly could about women and pregnancy to see if I could make sense of any of it. Naturally, it wouldn't be an easy task. I was only thirty-one years old and pretty much still saw women as objects. I wasn't yet wise enough to objectively scrutinize, indict, and understand women. I was

Many times you have to wait a half century to know if it is a boy or a girl—especially in our modern time.

still at the age when a woman is the most precious thing for a man, the only thing he wants, needs, and lives for. The time in a man's life when every little wish the woman wants is his command. To top it all off, I had already discovered that I knew nothing about women to begin with, so I had to start from scratch. But come hell or high water, I was determined that I would get to the bottom of it. What made me feel good was that for the first time since hearing that comment at the bar that night, I truly believed I knew what I had to do to figure out whether or not those words were true. The doctor, the midwife, and my own ideas about matters of wealth and superstitions had finally, I thought, put me on the right path.

Since those days in 1958 I spent the next thirty-five years thinking and researching this whole subject, this mystery surrounding women, their nature, and their offspring. Now that I've outlined how this whole thing began nearly four decades ago, I'm ready to share my findings with you. I hope that the mystery unfolds for you as you read the following pages, as it did for me over the years. I'll warn you up front that it will not be easy to understand, much less agree, with many of the things I have to say. At the very least I hope that someone, somewhere will at least begin to understand some of the things that I now hold as my utmost convictions.

Many surprises are in store for men and women alike in the following pages. Some may offend you, others may surprise you, while still others you'll swear you knew all along. In any case, they remain my convictions; and I challenge any and all of you to put them to the test, for in the end you'll have no choice but to agree with my findings. Notwithstanding all of the scientific, medical, and genetic research to date, it seems to me that my ideas remain sound, and if anyone disagrees, I would urge them to recheck or redo the research that is inconsistent with whatever they are exposed to in the following chapters.

2
ADOLESCENT GIRLS

It is a saying as old as time back in Italy. For all young newlyweds, the saying goes, "Congratulations, and hope you have baby boys." Obviously, if this ever actually occurred the species could not survive, but back in that part of the world this is exactly what every couple wants: little boys. This is not to say that little girls are not welcome, but when little girls are born to young couples the atmosphere is not the same. The celebrations are not as spirited. There is not as much dancing and rejoicing, and neither the party nor the cigars are as big. In all fairness, I can't sit here and say that this is so for all couples; but for the majority of them, when baby boys are born, all hell breaks loose, so to speak.

I should also point out that having baby boys is a more important event to the fathers than the mothers. For the mothers, be it a boy or a girl, it's their child nonetheless, and they'll love it just the same. In fact, even in Italy there are a small minority of mothers who actually prefer little girls to little boys; but for the men, even those who say they have no preference, you can bet a lot of money that they secretly would prefer a boy. A famous athlete explained the prevailing attitude in Italy best when he was asked how many children he had, and he answered "Seven failures and one boy!" To put it another way, to many couples in southern Italy little girls are like uninvited guests. Unlike packages, they cannot simply be sent back; therefore, an initial obligation develops in the parents which in time transforms into affection and love for the child. With boys, however, it's different. The triumph for the parents is immediate and total, right from the outset.

There are, I believe, some obvious and easily explicable reasons for this. First, in traditional Italian families, boys carry the family name and girls do not. It is unheard of in the old country for a woman to retain her maiden name after marriage. Rather, she accepts her husband's surname as her own, and the conception and birth of a baby boy is the only assurance that the name will carry on. Second, with respect to employment and economic opportunity, males are still way ahead of women in southern Italy. Hence, when a male is born into the family, the future economic stability of that family, and specifically the parents, is enhanced. If, on the other hand, a little girl is born, the traditional expectation is that she will someday marry a man, take on his family name, and depend on him for financial survival. Therefore, the girl's family will have raised a child that will be "given over," if you will, for the benefit of someone else. The logical endpoint with this type of argument is that the more boys the couple produces, the better off the family will be. There will be more assurance that the name will carry on, and also a better chance of a bright economic future for the immediate family in particular, and the whole family circle in general. This scenario is not only common in southern Italy but also in many, if not most, other countries around the world.

The situation may be a bit different in America, although I, for one, seriously doubt it. These days in the United States it is not uncommon for women to retain their maiden name after marriage, and I've even heard of some cases where the woman's children, including the boys, actually accept the mother's maiden name as their surname. Moreover, the employment situation for women in this country has changed in the past few decades. Today, women in modern western society enjoy an almost equal financial position to men so that their future is not as bleak as it once was, nor are the women totally dependent on men. Hence, couples in this country, and especially fathers, may not be as obsessed with having little boys as they are in southern Italy and other parts of the world. However, as I've stated, my gut feeling is that if everyone were honest with themselves, most individuals would still prefer boys in America as well. As we'll find out later, although this so-called women's movement has had many favorable consequences for women, it is at least partially, if not mostly, responsible for a radical change that is currently under way in the gender determination, social aberration, and overall traditional family destruction that is occurring in today's youth and nuclear family.

It turns out that the mystery to understanding and predicting what determines the gender of a particular child, the way that child will behave socially, and, if the child happens to be a girl, what type of children she will produce, is totally locked within the mind of the biological mother. However, in order to understand the complex mind of a mature woman, we need not only trace its development since infancy, but more importantly, we need to examine its development in that period of time between conception and birth. That is, we also need to understand the development of a girl's brain while she is in her mother's womb. This is because the mind of any individual woman is necessarily influenced by and through the nourishment and impulses she receives while in her mother's womb, in addition to all of the life experiences and environmental input she receives after birth. By this I do not mean to imply that little boys don't develop in the same way. Indeed, as we shall see later, impulses received by little boys from their mother during pregnancy also have severe consequences; but at the moment we are concerned with the development of a woman's brain only.

The reason why a woman's brain is so important to the discussion is because it is the woman's brain exclusively that determines the sex of her offspring. However, the extent to which a particular woman's brain has been affected by her mother's impulses during pregnancy and the environmental components that have influenced her over time, are extremely important with respect to her own mindset during pregnancy. It is these two factors that enable the woman alone to produce either a girl or a boy. In order to fully understand these phenomena it is probably easier to start with the environmental and external factors that influence little girls during their tender ages and then proceed by examining the motherly internal factors that are given to them by their mothers in the period of time between conception and birth. Although this may seem a bit backwards, it will, in my opinion, make it much easier to describe and understand the entire process that occurs inside of a woman's brain, which ultimately leads to gender determination in her offspring and subsequent development of the child.

It is well known that girls develop much faster than boys in the early stages of life, not only physically but mentally as well. While young boys are concerned with playing football out in the street or playing with their toys and their friends, young girls are already contemplating the more sophisticated aspects of life such as attracting the opposite sex and getting ready for motherhood. All one has to do is watch some of today's most popular, albeit trashy, talk shows like *Jenny Jones, Montel Williams, Jerry Springer* and so on to realize that girls are indeed much more sophisticated than their male counterparts at the early stages of life when it comes to sexual matters. Physically, it is not uncommon to see girls between the ages of ten to thirteen years of age that look like, or try to mimic, well developed women. If anyone disagrees with this, a simple glance at any magazine store will convince them otherwise. Today's magazine store shelves are loaded with magazines displaying sclantily clothed teenage girls full of provocative advertisements aimed at other teenage girls. And the makeup industry also has developed a tremendous market specifically geared for teenage and even pre-teenage girls. This is definitely not the case with young men. Whereas very young girls are aware of, and interested in, their own sex appeal, it would be fair to say that young boys of comparable age don't even have a clue as to what sex appeal is.

Conventional wisdom has it that although these young girls are physically mature and in some cases just as able to reproduce as women in their twenties and thirties, they are still mentally little children that are not yet able to understand the important things in life. I, for one, differ with this notion. Indeed, there is no doubt in my mind that most girls past the age of ten are light-years ahead of boys of the same age and are very well aware of the effect that they have on grown men who in some cases are many times their age.

The reasons for this, which we will examine in detail later, lie within the superior brain of the female, which has been influenced first and foremost by her mother. Therefore, it is not because of her actions that a female finds herself in a position superior to that of her male counterpart in the early stages of life, but rather the superiority is a natural consequence which has been given to her during her mother's pregnancy. The way this occurs, as we shall examine later, is through feminine impulses that are fed to her while in her mother's womb. These feminine impulses give the female child a brain and mindset that, from the very beginning, is much more superior than that of her male counterparts. From the very start she possesses superior intelligence in the ways of life and reproduction, a keener intuitive ability which enables her to better understand, and in many cases, completely dominate the opposite sex, a greater curiosity in those aspects of life concerned with lovemaking and intimate situations, and a more worldly awareness of her position in life and her unique abilities as a woman.

The early physical development of a woman is perhaps the most obvious characteristic that puts her in a superior position to that of a man early in life. A casual stroll on 8th Avenue in New York City's Manhattan borough will easily make a believer of any potential nonbeliever. Alternatively, anyone who has ever gone to any junior high school and compared the physical difference between girls in their early teens and boys in their early teens will easily know what I am talking about. As early as ten years old, girls are concerned with the proper application of make-up, wearing bras and stockings, wearing provocative clothing, and the best methods for attracting older boys. In contrast, their male counterparts are more worried about playing sports, being accepted by their male peers, and not at all concerned with their physical appearance or the opposite sex.

Many of these young girls are also exceptionally well developed. Most have developed breasts and hips by the tender age of thirteen. They shave their legs. They have already started their menstrual cycle, are already trained in the "facts of life" (mainly through discussions with their mothers and other female friends), and are very aware of their bodies. They go through painstaking measures to present their bodies in the best light possible, mainly to lure potential mates their way. They are not the least bit concerned with boys their own age because they know that in comparison to themselves, such boys know nothing about what they want, have probably never thought about it, and even if they did, they certainly don't know how to give it to them.

In contrast, boys between the ages of ten to fourteen or so know absolutely nothing about the needs of a woman, what it is that girls their own age really desire, or how to give it to them. They are not concerned about women at all. Although they may get together and tell tall tales during their male bonding sessions, each and every one of them knows that they are all telling lies. None of them really feel adequate with the girls and wouldn't have the slightest idea of what to do with girls their own age if they actually ever had the chance to have an intimate encounter with them. Physically they still look like little boys. Most of them that age don't yet shave, they still dress like little boys, are considered little boys by their female counterparts, and not knowing what to do about it, they continue to act like little boys because they realize that they are no match, physically or otherwise, for their female peers. Unlike the girls, they do not receive glances or, better yet, stares from the opposite sex because physically and sexually they still have absolutely nothing to offer, and all of the girls their age already know this. Indeed, even in those very rare cases where a young boy has shown signs of physical maturity due to early shaving or early muscular development, the result is the same because the young girls know that mentally the boy could not even begin to understand the kinds of things that she has in mind.

This disparity in physical development also manifests itself in the reproductive readiness and ability of the two sexes. The daily newspapers are full of actual cases of girls as young as ten or eleven years old giving birth to little boys and little girls. However, it is very rare indeed to read stories about really young boys fathering children. Usually these young girls are impregnated by much older men, who are attracted to them because of their womanly charms, which they have studied, contemplated, mastered, developed and exhibited very early in life. This is a natural consequence of the above noted early physical development of women, their preoccupation with making themselves attractive to the opposite sex, and their striving for male attention, coupled with the inadequacy and late development of boys their own age.

Aside from their physical superiority, young girls also have a mental advantage over young boys when it comes to sex, love, and the facts of life. Put simply, this is because their curiosity and

The boy could not even begin to understand the kinds of things that she has in mind.

their ability to understand these matters early in life is superior to that of their male counterpart. When it comes to the topic of reproduction of the species, women possess an unlimited potential that is enhanced by superior intuition and unlimited intelligence, which is much more powerful than those of men even twice their age. While little boys (and young men, for that matter) are concerned about putting a basketball through a hoop, girls are instead more worried about trying out their mother's new lipstick or trying on some sexy garter belts at the local Victoria's Secret outlet. When the boys are playing stickball at the local courtyard and getting into fights over the score, the girls are carefully studying the latest make-up techniques outlined in the new issue of *Seventeen* magazine and trying to figure out what blush would best be suited for their skin tone. While the boys are sitting around discussing the statistics of their athletic heroes, the young girls are hanging out at each other's houses talking about their latest date with the older man that they met through a mutual friend.

These conversations are not sexually benign. On the contrary, young girls will sit back and tell each other every conceivable detail about the affair they had. They'll talk about how far he went, how long he lasted, how far they actually wanted him to go, whether or not he was adequate, if he knew what he was doing, whether they'll see him again, et cetera. They'll exchange tips with each other about how to get him more worked up the next time so that he'll desire them more, how to dress so as to make themselves irresistible, and how to insure that he will not be interested in anyone else but them. Mind you, all these discussions that are taking place are usually among girls between the ages of ten to fourteen or fifteen or so, but the men they are discussing in many cases are in their twenties or even thirties.

If anybody believes that all of this is far-fetched, I would encourage them to find out what percentage of girls under age fifteen have been with older men over twenty, and then compare that number to the percentage of boys under the age of fifteen that have been with women over the age of twenty. I think you'll get the message immediately. It's also true that some may say this is because older men prey on younger women more than the other way around; but pedophiles aside, older men are not really interested in young women unless they come equipped with womanly charms, both physically and otherwise. And most men, if they really want to be honest, will readily admit that.

As we shall see in more detail later, this is the direct result of feminine chemical impulses that are supplied from the mother to her daughter while she is still in the womb. These chemical impulses in effect predetermine the social evolution of little girls though adolescence and young womanhood. Which takes us to the second aspect of this phenomenon that I spoke of earlier; that is, the internal factors (i.e. those not due to social and environmental factors) that shape the difference between adolescent girls and boys. These are largely controlled and governed by the internal impulses that the children received while they were still in the mother's womb. Without getting ahead of ourselves in the discussion, these internal impulses may easily be explained in the following way. When a woman becomes pregnant, her body produces hormones that affect the embryo in many different ways. This is nothing new and has been known for a long time. Indeed, the latest studies suggest that such hormones play a much more significant role during pregnancy than was previously thought. The logical extension of such findings forms part of the basis of my thesis, which simply adds the following: not only do the hormones and other chemical compounds produced by the mother during pregnancy affect the genetic and physical aspects of the offspring, but they also determine precisely how that child, whether male or female, will develop socially and sexually even before they are born.

What this means is that these hormones and chemical impulses are given directly from the mother to the child during the embryonic stage, and the process is irreversible, socially, environmentally, or otherwise after birth. Moreover, with respect to the development of the child, these maternal impulses are far more important than the social and peer-induced factors discussed above. Hence, if during pregnancy, the mother provides overwhelmingly feminine hormonal impulses to the child, the end product will be a feminine offspring, whether physically male or female. Conversely, if an expectant mother supplies mainly masculine hormonal impulses to the fetus, then the result will be a masculine offspring, regardless of the actual sex of the child. This, of course, does not answer the question as to how it is that a woman determines the actual sex of the child, which we will examine in a later chapter; but it does provide the necessary stepping stone that we need to answer that question, because it provides an explanation for the many diverse sexual orientations that various people exhibit.

For example, if a pregnant woman is carrying a baby boy (again, we'll examine how this comes to be in the following chapter) and she provides that baby boy with overwhelmingly male hormonal impulses throughout the pregnancy, the result will be a "normal" baby boy. If, on the other hand, the same mother supplies that same fetus with predominantly feminine hormonal impulses, then the result will be an effeminate male child or a "sissy." Similarly, if a pregnant woman is carrying a baby girl and she provides her with strong feminine hormonal impulses, the result will be a "normal" baby girl. However, if she supplies that same fetus with masculine hormonal impulses, then the result will be a masculine girl or a "tomboy." Once this maternal contribution is completed, the personal and behavioral characteristics of the child are pretty much complete and set in stone, so to speak. And, even though there will be some additional contribution from that child's peers, environmental surroundings, and social interactions, the basic personality traits of that person, from a sexual perspective, are complete at birth.

Hence a "normal boy" will congregate with other "normal boys," and together they will reinforce those traits that "normal boys" have in common, such as sports, playing games, et cetera. Similarly, "normal girls" will congregate with other "normal girls," and they will reinforce among themselves those traits that they have in common, namely making themselves irresistible for the sole purpose of attracting the men that they want. Sissies and tomboys will also congregate with other sissies and tomboys. Unfortunately, because of the social taboos, particularly with respect to "sissies," coupled with their relative minority within the general population, this may not occur until much later in life when that person (whether an effeminate male or a butch girl) becomes comfortable enough and courageous enough to go out and seek other individuals more like themselves. As we will see later, in many cases these children will develop later in life into bisexual males or females, homosexuals, or lesbians. But it goes without saying that their sexual orientation has little to do with environmental factors and everything to do with their mother's hormonal supply.

Several observations that fall out of the explanation above are worthy of note, because they shed light on several phenomena for which there appears to be no easy explanation. First, if we accept the notion that sexual preference is actually determined while the future child is still within his mother's womb, then it should be clear that the sexual orientation of any given individual is not due to environmental influences at all. Instead, it is an "inherited" trait, if you will, given directly and exclusively to him or her from the mother during pregnancy. The heterosexual, bisexual, or homosexual orientation of any given individual simply reflects the degree of opposite sex hormonal supply that the mother gave that child during the term of the pregnancy. Second, the whole concept of transsexualism is also easily understood through the above noted argument, because it merely represents the tension between the internally inherited maternal hormones an individual has received prior to birth pitted against the social and environmental influences he or she is influenced by during adolescence. Hence, a biological boy who has received large amounts of feminine impulses from his mother will naturally feel like a girl trapped in a boy's body during adolescence, and eventually, for peace of mind, may wish to become a woman later in life. Third, the apparent solitude which many bisexuals, homosexuals and transsexuals often report early in life is also understandable because feeling "different from within," they naturally find it harder to identify with any of their peers early in life and literally have to wait until adulthood to seek out others like themselves before they feel comfortable with their sexuality.

It should be clear at this point that the maternal hormones are really the controlling factor in sexual development because they are produced by the mother, and they shape and control the child. The paternal input is masculine and unimportant. Whereas the male sperm supplies a genetic code through chromosomal pairs and DNA, the contribution ends there. This is because once the sperm impregnates the female egg (and I'll have much more to say about this later), it is the female who has total and exclusive control through her body and chemical make-up to manipulate the fertilized egg. Therefore, the male contribution is an instantaneous event and a one time transfer of genetic material, whereas the female influence over that same fertilized egg is, in contrast, much more lengthy, continuous, and conducive to manipulation through her exclusive bodily chemistry.

For the purposes of the present discussion, this is important because it easily explains why fraternal twins may have totally separate and distinct sexual orientations, yet contain a similar genetic code. This is because one of the fertilized eggs may be nourished by female maternal hormones exclusively, for example, whereas the other may be nourished by varying amounts of a masculine hormone as well as a female hormone. Moreover, such a theory may also explain the apparently different sexual orientation in identical twins, which has been reported in various studies and remains, understandably, more problematic. The theory, however, may explain such a situation in the following way. One portion of a fertilized egg may be differentially affected by maternal hormones during pregnancy such that half the egg may receive larger or smaller amounts of hormonal supplements than the other portion; it is possible that half the egg may produce a heterosexual child whereas the other half may produce a child that later exhibits bisexual, transsexual, or homosexual behavior.

Of course, the exact mechanism by which the latter phenomena may occur is outside the scope of this discussion. I am certainly not trained in medicine, genetics, physiology, biology, or physiochemical mechanisms of the human body. However, it seems to me that there must be some method available to explain exactly how different portions of a growing embryo may be affected differently while in the mother's womb. If this explanation currently exists (or if it doesn't, once it is found), the whole problem of differential sexual orientation in identical twins would, in my opinion, be solved once and for all. Perhaps this would make a wonderful research project for some doctoral student at one of the nation's major university medical centers.

Hopefully, I've succeeded in explaining why it is that, at least according to my thesis, maternal impulses supplied during pregnancy and social interactions with girlfriends during adolescence provide the blueprint for all of a young woman's subsequent actions later in life. At least with respect to sexual orientation, sexual development, and (as we shall see later) gender selection for her own offspring, these are the only factors that need to be considered because they are the only ones that influence a young woman. One point that needs clarification, however, is this: the social and environmental factors play a very small, if not insignificant role, with respect to a woman's attitude toward the opposite sex and her ability to control and determine the gender of her offspring. As noted earlier, although these outside influences may be relatively significant to girls who have received significant amounts of predominantly male hormonal impulses and, as a result, have difficulty adjusting to societal norms, it is not so in the ordinary case. Hence, assuming that any given girl has been provided with overwhelming feminine impulses while in her mother's womb during pregnancy, that is all she needs to develop into a very powerful being who will be able to control not only any man she desires, but also will be able to determine whether she will provide him with a boy, a girl, a tomboy, a sissy, a bisexual, a lesbian girl, a homosexual boy, or even a transsexual offspring. Exactly how this occurs is the subject of the next chapter.

3

PREPARING FOR MATRIMONY AND BEARING CHILDREN

It's one of the most fascinating transformations in nature, and it occurs during the time a girl develops into a young woman. As I discussed earlier, when parents are first confronted with the fact that their child will be a girl, almost invariably they will be less enthusiastic about it than if it were going to be a boy. Regardless of whether or not they admit it, this is almost always the case, particularly for the father. However, unbeknownst to them, their new girl will ultimately grow up to be a very coveted woman indeed, for the right man. This transformation from "second best" to "highly coveted" begins when the girl starts developing into a young woman, but truly blossoms when she is ready to find her mate in life.

When women start seriously pondering the idea of finding themselves a mate and contemplating marriage, they become the most powerful and dangerous entities known to man. At this time in their life, they possess a sort of unlimited strength over men that is hard to explain. The power they hold over men is capable of making the man do some of the most absurd things one could think of, like spending all of his money and possessions, compromising his career, putting his own life on the line, or taking the life of another, all for the mere purpose of getting the woman's undivided attention.

In order to accurately understand this power, we must first separate society into two distinct groups: the first group consists of the powerful, the ultra-rich, and the intellectuals (including powerful politicians, wealthy doctors and lawyers, successful artists, musicians, writers, et cetera), and the second group consists of the remainder of the general population (including the relatively uneducated, the factory worker, the laborer, et cetera). With respect to the first group, politicians will risk their careers, musicians will write songs, writers will write novels, artists will create immortal works of art, the rich may spend thousands of dollars, all for a simple smile or other similar gratification from the woman who has managed to capture their attention. With respect to the second group, just about anything goes for the woman who has captured their heart; although they may not possess the money or skills for extravagances, the men in this category may resort to violent behavior, commit unspeakable crimes, fight till the death, and risk their own lives, just to gain the attention and affection of the woman they want.

In this period of her life, the woman is the center of existence for all "normal" young men. She represents a dream that must become reality at all costs. For the opposite sex, she is the pinnacle of happiness; regardless of anything else that the man may have going for him (fabulous career, money, fame, et cetera), it is all meaningless, unless he can share it with her. She knows that she alone is, and will always remain, the center of his life, because she's the one who will be able to produce offspring for him, and that is what he'll ultimately want most out of life.

By this time a woman knows that when it comes to the reproduction of the species she is in absolute control. She knows that she's the one that must put all of her energy into bearing the child and that the birth of the child will all be on her shoulders, so to speak. For the man, from a practical perspective, the reproduction of the species represents pure enjoyment and nothing else. He does not have to carry the child for nine months, his body does not have to be subjected to hormonal imbalance and physical deformity, his life will not be disrupted at all. His role is simply to provide sperm for the woman and let her take care of the rest. Because she knows this, this gives her enormous control and power not only over her man, but over the offspring as well. More importantly, as I explain in detail below, this power actually gives her the ability to manipulate the gender and sexual identity of the offspring in a fascinating and mind-boggling way.

In order to understand exactly how this works from the beginning, let us try to imagine that first instant when a single man and a single woman meet, lightning strikes, and they "fall

He has chosen his woman. In actuality, the exact opposite has occurred. It is the woman who has chosen her man.

in love," so to speak. This is commonly perceived by most people as a time when a man has finally finished "sowing his oats," has chosen his woman, and is now ready to finally settle down and be with her. In actuality, the exact opposite has occurred. It is the woman that has chosen her man and not the other way around. She is the one who has finally decided that a particular man is for her, and not vice versa. If at this time the woman decides to let go of her man, ninety-nine percent of the time he will be unsuccessful in trying to change her mind. As for the other one percent, if the man keeps trying and is actually capable of convincing the woman to remain with him, the results will almost always be disastrous. In any case, this scenario is not germane at this point of our discussion.

Once the woman has chosen her man, she begins collecting information about him and storing it in a part of her brain for future use and consumption. It's important to realize from the outset that this data-gathering stage begins immediately after the woman chooses her man. From the moment she realizes that this is the man she wants, one portion of her brain does nothing else but collect and store information about him, including the most insignificant, miniscule details. She must know everything about him—how he speaks, how he dresses, how much money he makes, what he does for a living, whether or not he's educated, how he reacts in given situations, whether or not he listens to her, if he's gentle, what his vices are, and an infinite number of other details. Not one single comma can be left out when it comes to knowing everything about her man. If she's not in a position to find out some of the things she needs to know, she'll use other resources to find out and investigate. This process continues throughout the time the courtship progresses and will not stop until she decides that she has no more need to do so, which occurs when, and only when, she's convinced that she knows everything about him.

In contrast, the man is totally unaware about what's going on during this time. While he's concentrating on courting her and kissing her and caressing her, he's totally oblivious to the intense scrutiny he's being subjected to. During this period of time, the more he persists, the more she resists. The more he insists, the more she withdraws. The more he corrects his courting behavior, the more aloof she becomes. He is totally unaware at this time that he's under the microscope, so to speak, and the more desperately he tries, the more he allows her to read him like a book, which is exactly what she's trying to do.

This data-gathering behavior becomes extremely important in sexual matters as well, as one might expect. Hence, even though during this courting phase of the relationship the woman has the same sexual desires that the man does, she's much better at controlling those desires. Therefore, while he gets all worked up trying to "show his love for her," she has the ability to remain relatively aloof, simply observing and storing information that she'll be able to use at a later time when she has finally learned everything there is to know, and therefore will know how and when to use the information that she gained, especially the information that she has about him in the bedroom.

All of this may not make sense to the men who are reading this book, probably because they've never really stopped to think about it. But I'm here to tell you that during this period of time, this is exactly and exclusively what the woman is doing and thinking about. To be sure, this whole data-gathering stage really begins when a female first begins to develop into a young woman, but as I've mentioned, it really blossoms and becomes acute when she starts considering matrimony. What's more important is that it doesn't end then. Rather, it continues throughout the time she is being courted, united with her chosen man in matrimony, and finally becomes an expectant mother. At this time the data-gathering process becomes crucial because everything that she has learned about her man up to that point is directly related to, as we shall learn, whether she will bear him male children, female children, or, to use an overly broad, generic phrase, abnormal children.

The reason for all this information gathering and storing that the woman performs is really in preparation for the new family that she will create. After all, that is the only reason why she chose the man that she did in the first place. She chose her particular man because she thought that he would be the best one suited for providing her with the kind of family and children she wants. However, the information she gathers and stores will, unbeknownst to her, have a direct impact on the children she will create. Therefore, in a sense, our destiny in life is already in the process of being decided even before our mothers have been impregnated by the men in their life. They don't know this, of course, but there's no doubt, as we shall see, that this is exactly what's happening.

Conventional wisdom has it that women look for the following characteristics in their mates: education, wealth, physical beauty, physical ability, character, intelligence, courage, and success. This is probably a pretty accurate list, although I suspect that there may be a host of other characteristics not included on this list which, nonetheless, would be pretty important to some women. Hence, when the woman is carefully scrutinizing her future partner, these are the things she's paying attention to, in addition to a host of other minor details that may be of particular importance to her. What I'm here to tell you is this—if, during her pregnancy, the woman becomes aware that what she has concluded about one of her mate's characteristics is in fact incorrect, she has the ability to control the environment of the growing embryo in such a way that she can determine, without her even knowing about it, whether the embryo will develop into a male, a female, a lesbian, a homosexual, a transsexual, or an individual having some other confused sexual identity. Therefore, in a sense, our destiny as sexual beings is predestined in some cases even before conception by the mother's preconceived ideas of her mate's characteristics.

I realize that this is a pretty bold statement. Some of you may think that it's a totally absurd conclusion, but that is the thesis of this book plain and simple. Some people may find this idea offensive. I apologize in advance to you, but I nevertheless stick to my premise. Others may conclude that this idea has no medical and scientific basis to it, but I assure you that my theory is, at the very least, consistent with all of the most recent medical findings. Moreover, for those of you who ridicule my suggestion on these or other grounds, I invite you to read on before making a final judgment.

In order to understand how a woman determines the gender and sexual orientation of a child, it is important to understand that a particular couple must be analyzed as a closed system. In other words, the same woman with a different man may produce different offspring than those she will produce with her chosen mate. Similarly, if the man in question had ended up with a different woman, the results may likewise be different.

Therefore, we must be clear from the outset that to understand the process of sexual identity determination, we must restrict ourselves to a particular couple. In other words, I am not suggesting in any way that regardless of the man a woman chooses she will have the ability of producing all females or all males, depending on what she wishes. What I am saying is that once a woman and a man have united, she alone determines the gender and sexual orientation of the children, depending on her perceptions of the mate she is with.

For the purposes of this discussion I will not concern myself with the atypical relationships that are all too commonplace in today's society. Instead, the focus will be on the more traditional setting where a man and a woman fall in love, marry, and then decide to start a family together. That is not to say that the thesis discussed here is not applicable in those other cases as well, but I will stick to the more traditional situation because it is still the most common, and in any case is the one I am most familiar with and, therefore, the one I am more comfortable exploring and describing.

Once a couple get married and the honeymoon portion of the relationship is over, the routine portion of life takes over, and with it the minor irritations and idiosyncrasies of the two individuals in the relationship start manifesting themselves. Of course, as I pointed out earlier, by this time the woman already knows all of the habits, strengths and weaknesses of her partner because she has been carefully scrutinizing him for quite some time. The difference is that during this phase of the relationship she starts paying closer attention to the more subtle, everyday attributes of her mate, such as whether he snores too loud or not at all, doesn't shower enough or too much, the way he interacts and communicates with her when making decisions such as what kind of toilet paper to buy, and other relatively trivial matters. These observations continue on a daily basis, and it is exactly these observations, coupled with the other ones that she has accumulated throughout her relationship with her mate which I spoke of earlier, that have a direct impact on the type of offspring she produces for him when she finally becomes impregnated with his sperm. Exactly how this occurs is the thesis of this book and the subject of the next chapter.

4

HOW WOMEN DETERMINE THE SEX OF THEIR OFFSPRING

During the past few decades incredible advances have been made in medical and genetic research. We now know, for example, that DNA contains the complete genetic code for any given human being. We also know that female eggs contain only XX chromosomes whereas male sperm cells have both X and Y chromosomes. Advancements in technology have also enabled us to actually observe a growing embryo during the very early stages of life. In fact, recent articles in reputable magazines such as *Time* have published actual pictures of 20-day-old embryos that have enabled doctors to track a growing fetus from virtual conception to birth.

Given these advances, many researchers and medical experts have demonstrated that it is actually the men who determine the sex of their children because without the Y chromosome contribution, creating male offspring is impossible. This has been confirmed by the so-called test tube fertilization technology of recent years. The common denominator in all of these advancements and studies has been this: if there is no Y chromosome contribution, the result will be a female fetus, period. Moreover, given that males are the only ones that have Y chromosomes to contribute, it logically follows that males are the only ones capable of determining the sex of their children. Hence, if a female is impregnated with the X chromosome of the male, the result will be a female child. Conversely, if the female egg is penetrated by the Y chromosome of the male, the result will be a male fetus one hundred percent of the time.

The latest research, conducted at the Genetics & IVF Institute in Fairfax, Virginia, also shows that gender selection may actually be a possibility in a laboratory setting because sperm that carry the Y chromosome contain less genetic material than sperm carrying X chromosomes. This new discovery suggests that it is theoretically possible to selectively isolate Y-carrying sperm from X-carrying sperm, thereby ensuring the sex of a baby by fertilizing a female egg with either a Y sperm or an X sperm through systematic isolation of the preferred sperm type. As if that weren't enough, the study suggests that sex determination through this method is already under way. According to the initial trial runs, gender selection will be synthetically possible (for couples who can afford it) as soon as the sperm selection process is refined.

At first glance, these advancements and genetic studies seem to demonstrate in no uncertain terms that it is the male, not the female, who is responsible for determining the gender of any given offspring. In fact, as I will demonstrate to you, the opposite is actually true. Although I know that there is really no way to dispute all of the latest research (not only because of my total ignorance with respect to genetic knowledge, but also because of the total agreement of these facts within the scientific community), it is also my conviction that it is the female, not the male, that actually determines the sex of a baby. Furthermore, I am confident that I can demonstrate this to be the case, notwithstanding the findings of the medical and scientific research. Before I do that, however, it would be helpful to review the process by which a female egg actually becomes fertilized, in an effort to demonstrate how it is possible and, in fact, much more plausible for the female to accomplish the gender determination of her offspring, despite the genetic restrictions and contradictory medical and clinical studies. The foregoing discussion may seem to be a bit complicated, and downright boring to some. Nonetheless, it is of vital importance for a thorough understanding of the subject matter. Although I've tried to keep it as elementary as possible, I apologize in advance and ask that all of you bear with me for the next few pages.

In order to fully understand the process, it is important to keep in mind from the outset that a singe male sperm cell does not carry an X and a Y chromosome. Rather, each individual sperm cell carries either an X chromosome or a Y chromosome. That's the reason why a woman can have twins of a different gender. For example, if two male sperm cells, one containing a Y chromosome and one containing an X chromosome, fertilize a female egg, the result will be a set of twins where one is a boy and one is a girl. On the other hand, if two sperm cells each containing Y chromosomes each fertilize an egg, the result will be a set of twin boys. It is also true, and worth noting, that in the case of identical twins, only one sperm cell, containing either an X chromosome or a Y chromosome, actually fertilizes the egg. After the fertilization process occurs, the egg splits into two parts and gives rise to two children instead of one. That's why in the case of identical twins, the result is twins of the same gender.

What this means is that although it is true that the male sperm determines the sex of the child in a technical sense, it is nonetheless possible (and, I submit, much more plausible) for the woman to actually determine the sex of the offspring by selecting which of the male sperm cells will more readily or more easily fertilize her eggs. This process, which I call "selective fertilization," is a simple one to describe and envision. The main difference between my version of "selective fertilization" and the "selective fertilization" referred to in the genetic studies conducted at the Genetics & IVF Institutes noted above—and it is a critical one—is that in my version of selectivity is accomplished through a totally natural process that happens spontaneously, whereas in the clinical version sex determination can only be accomplished through genetic intervention and manipulation of the fertilization process itself.

Perhaps the best way to describe this "natural selective fertilization" process which I am talking about is to try and envision exactly what occurs, biologically speaking, during the conception process. During intercourse a man ejaculates and discharges millions of sperm cells, which all start swimming towards the female egg in an effort to fertilize it. Most die off, and only a few actually survive the journey to the egg. Once the sperm cells arrive at their destination, one of the cells (and, more rarely, two or three) will actually be successful in penetrating and fertilizing the egg, leading to the formation of an embryo and a new fetus and, ultimately, a new life. If the successful sperm contains a Y chromosome, the fetus will be a male fetus. If, on the other hand, the fertilizing sperm is carrying an X chromosome, the result will be a female fetus. So far, all of this is consistent with the scientific explanation of the gender determination of the fetus.

I submit, however, that what the scientific community has overlooked is exactly why some sperm cells are successful in penetrating the female egg and others are not. I propose that the natural fertilization process whereby a sperm cell impregnates a woman's egg is not a random occurrence. Rather, the penetrating sperm is successful precisely because of a particular environment that the woman has created around that egg. For example, in some cases a sperm carrying a Y chromosome is more successful in penetrating the egg than a sperm carrying an X chromosome because the woman has created an environment around her egg which makes it easier for the Y-carrying sperm to penetrate that environment than for the X-carrying sperm to penetrate it. Hence, the female is capable of creating an environmental envelope, if you will, around the unfertilized egg that is naturally capable of selectively determining which sperm will fertilize it by scrutinizing between the X and Y carriers. The environment is such that all X-chromosome sperm carriers are essentially filtered out, so to speak, while Y-chromosome sperm carriers are allowed to go through, and vice versa.

I am not a genetic or medical expert and, therefore, I cannot offer the biological or physiochemical details of how exactly this phenomenon occurs, but what I can say is that there are many reasons to believe that it does, some of which have a scientific basis and some of which do not. And although I cannot explain the biochemical mechanism by which this "natural selective fertilization" occurs, I can explain why a woman creates such a "gender-hostile environment" or "gender-inviting environment," depending on her thought processes governing her feelings toward her mate.

The idea is quite simple, really. As we already know, there are certain unexplainable impulses which originate within a woman's brain during pregnancy that have considerable influence on the offspring she will produce. The subject of these so-called "personality genes" has received considerable attention of late, and researchers have shown that there are certain strange connections between a potential mother's thought processes and the resulting characteristics of her offspring. In fact, molecular biologist Dean Hammer of the

National Institutes of Health has been exploring such "scientific oddities" which appear to govern the very core of human individuality. The current suggestion is that certain heretofore undiscovered maternal genes may be responsible for some traits exhibited by newborns which would otherwise be inexplicable. (See, for example, the *Time Magazine* article, April 27, 1998, pp. 60-61.) Whether spontaneous brain-induced impulses, maternal genes as Dr. Hammer tells us, or as yet unexplained maternal genetic energy are at work, the end-product is clear. Mothers have much more to do with their offspring than previously thought—much, much, more, I propose. The mothers not only shape the characteristics of the offspring after conception, as these studies suggest, but, more importantly, it is the premise of my theory that the mothers also shape the characteristics of their offspring, including their gender and sexual orientation, both before conception and during the gestation period, respectively, while the growing embryo is within the mother's womb.

Brain-induced impulses, be they impulses, hormones, or some type of special genetic energy (for lack of a more sophisticated scientific term) triggered by a mother's thought processes, serve not only as a basis for determining the future characteristics of a child, as Dr. Hammer suggests, but also as a basis for producing a special external environment around the mother's egg, which will either facilitate or inhibit fertilization by particular sperm cells. If this energy produced by a mother's thought processes is predominantly feminine energy, then the egg's surrounding external environment will filter out or inhibit Y-chromosome sperm cells from penetrating the environmental envelope, thus ensuring fertilization by an X-carrying sperm, eventually resulting in the birth of a little girl. If, on the other hand, these thought-triggered impulses, hormones, or genetic energy is predominantly male, the egg's surrounding external environment will filter out X-chromosome sperm cell penetration and will preferentially allow Y-chromosome fertilization, thereby resulting in the birth of a little boy.

The determination of which external environment is created around the female egg is exclusively made by the woman and is intimately connected to the woman's perception of her mate. The male has absolutely nothing to do with it, whether he likes it or not. In general terms, if the woman has a very favorable opinion of her man, she will produce a feminine-hostile environment around the egg, which will inhibit X-chromosome penetration. If, on the other hand, the woman has an unfavorable opinion of her mate, then X-chromosome sperm cells will be preferred by the egg's environment. From this perspective, it is easy to see that although it is a technical truism that the male Y-chromosome carrying sperm is needed to produce a male offspring, it is actually the female that determines whether a Y-carrying sperm or an X-carrying sperm will fertilize her egg. Therefore, from a practical standpoint, she is the true determinator of the offspring's gender.

It is important to note several things at this juncture. First, the environment production stage is not an instantaneous event. The woman does not just get up on a particular day and decide that she will create a given environment so that she may give birth to males or females. In fact, she doesn't even know about the process at all. Rather, the production of the environment is a continuous process which develops over time by a steady stream of chemical impulses, or genetic energy, which is transmitted directly to the immediate surroundings of all potential eggs (i.e. to the reproductive system). The energy itself is produced by a woman's thought processes, which in turn produce the necessary brain impulses that eventually catalyze the creation of the environment.

Another important point to keep in mind is that these impulses that are sent to the reproductive system are not due to any ordinary and general thought processes that the woman may have. Instead, they are the specific result, and product of, a woman's thought processes regarding her individual synthesis of her mate's characteristics which have evolved throughout the length of their relationship. As such, these impulses are continuously created through a subconscious effort on her part, and she is wholly unaware of the biochemical processes that are occurring.

Finally, it is also important to point out that these thought processes that give rise to the brain impulses and hormonal activity are not necessarily homogeneous. In other words, whereas some of the woman's thoughts and perceptions about her mate may be advantageous to a Y-chromosome preferred environment, others may be hostile to a Y-chromosome environment. These different impulses may, therefore, produce a type of tension-filled, heterogeneous environment, which may in turn lead to a weak albeit Y-preferred environment or a weak albeit X-preferred environment. These latter situations will ultimately lead to a genetic boy having relatively weak male characteristics (e.g., timid, impotent, asexual, bisexual, transsexual, homosexual), or a genetic girl with weak female characteristics (e.g., tomboy, frigid, bisexual, lesbian). The accompanying diagram, shown in Figure 1, illustrates the above-noted environments with their corresponding offspring results.

Another important thing to note is that once the preconception environment is determined, it effects not only the unfertilized egg's surrounding, but also the subsequent environment of the mother's womb and, therefore, the growing fetus after fertilization takes place. In the general case, the environment will remain the same during the gestation period as it was during the preconception period and simply reinforce the fetus after the gender of the offspring has been determined. However, it is altogether possible that substantial changes in the woman's thought processes and perceptions of her mate during the gestation period may trigger very different impulses, which may drastically change the environment of the womb and the fetus during pregnancy, thereby leading to immediate and possibly severe changes in the characteristics of the offspring. These changes, although relatively rare, will be incapable of changing the sex of the fetus, and will usually exhibit themselves in the sexual orientation of the child or, on very rare occasions, by way of mental and physical handicaps.

How Women Create Selective Environments

As the scientific community is slowly finding out, there is an unexplainable connection between a mother's thought processes and the resulting characteristics of her offspring. What they still don't know is that thought processes have many more consequences than they presently realize. Specifically, what the scientific community still hasn't discovered is that a woman's thought processes, specifically those which are directly related to her opinion of her man, enable her, and her alone, to exclusively determine the sex of her child.

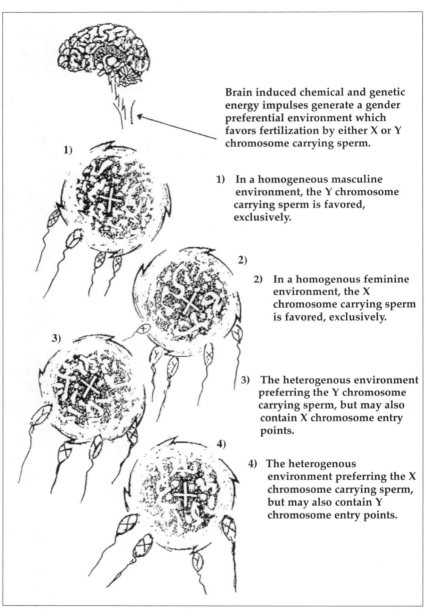

Brain induced chemical and genetic energy impulses generate a gender preferential environment which favors fertilization by either X or Y chromosome carrying sperm.

1) In a homogeneous masculine environment, the Y chromosome carrying sperm is favored, exclusively.

2) In a homogenous feminine environment, the X chromosome carrying sperm is favored, exclusively.

3) The heterogenous environment preferring the Y chromosome carrying sperm, but may also contain X chromosome entry points.

4) The heterogenous environment preferring the X chromosome carrying sperm, but may also contain Y chromosome entry points.

Figure 1: The Four Environments

Homogenous environments will produce solid masculine or feminine offspring. Heterogenous environments will produce weak masculine or feminine offspring, having traits of the other gender.

This natural gender selection process, as I've already stated, is accomplished through the creation of an environment surrounding the woman's eggs that is triggered by impulses of energy which she sends from her brain directly to the egg's location. These impulses, constantly relayed from the woman's brain to her reproductive system over time, serve to either allow or inhibit entry of particular sperm cells that ultimately control the gender that will be created. In addition, the specific impulses responsible for creating a determinative environment are directly related to her perceptions and opinions of her man.

Obviously an infinite number of factors shape a given woman's perception of her man and, consequently, an exhaustive list of these factors is impossible to produce. However, a typical example may be useful to illustrate the point.

The most obvious of these is the following: a less-than-handsome man marries a beautiful woman who absolutely adores him and loves him wholeheartedly. To her, he is nothing less than a Rudolph Valentino incarnate, together with all of the emotional characteristics and personality traits that she was seeking in a man all along. In fact, the man is relatively ugly, and by anybody else's standards he is emotionally bankrupt and lacks even the most fundamental skills of etiquette and social interaction. To the woman, however, this does not matter, because for all intents and purposes, to her he is nothing short of a polished and well groomed gentleman. Assuming that her perceptions about her man remain unchanged over time, that woman will produce as many male offspring as her mate desires, not because he wants them, but simply because of what she thinks of him.

Some generalizations can be made in determining what the likely outcome would be when a woman having a particular mindset ends up uniting with a particular man. The list below tabulates some of these generalizations. However, it is important to note that the following are just guidelines and may not be one-hundred percent accurate each and every time, simply because of the great number of intangible factors that may be at work with respect to any given couple.

a. All other things being equal, a woman who considers herself very beautiful and feels that her husband is not really worthy of her will generally produce female offspring because she will build an environment around her eggs that will inhibit her husband's Y-chromosome sperm from penetrating.

b. All other things being equal, a particular woman whose husband is intellectually superior and more intelligent than she is, and who perceives him as such will generally produce male offspring by generating a Y-chromosome friendly environment.

c. All other things being equal, a woman who believes herself to come from a higher class or more sophisticated background than her husband will generally produce female offspring.

d. A woman who perceives her man as a very strict, authoritative, but fair husband will produce an environment around her eggs which will be much more conducive to producing male offspring.

e. A woman who considers herself superior to others, is relatively narcissistic, and believes that she should always be the center of attention will generally produce female offspring.

f. All other things being equal, a woman who believes herself to be intellectually superior and more educated that her man will generally produce female offspring.

g. A woman who is overly ambitious, coquettish, and believes her husband (as well as the world) owes her something will generally produce female offspring.

h. A woman who believes her man to be a sort of a superman, physically or otherwise, will generally produce male offspring, regardless of whether he perceives himself the same way.

i. A woman who knows her man to be rough and of few but meaningful words will generally produce male offspring (although there are many exceptions in these cases).

j. A woman who marries an otherwise common man who then becomes very successful through his own ability and hard work will generally produce male offspring, if she is also convinced that it was truly her husband's sheer will power and abilities that led up to his good fortune.

Although these guidelines are valid in a general sense, the important thing to note is that everything depends on what the woman thinks of her man and not the other way around. Therefore, the following important factors must also be considered whenever any particular situation is being scrutinized. For example:

a. All of the advanced degrees, intellect, and education of the man will not matter if the woman believes herself to be of superior intellect and abilities. In such cases, only X-chromosome friendly environments should be expected.

b. A man's familial background, even if royal, will be meaningless if the woman believes her background to be superior to his.

c. A man's affection, respect, consideration, thoughtfulness, et cetera, will be utterly useless in formulating her opinions about him if she believes them to be ultimately done for ulterior motives, or are generally insincere.

d. All of the man's money, riches, and extravagances will have no importance in shaping her perceptions if she does not value such things or believes she can do without them.

e. All of the man's fairness and gentlemanly demeanor will be counterproductive if she is inwardly a rebel.

f. All of a man's roughness, toughness, and machismo will work against him if she hates him.

With all of this in mind, it is easy to see that the overriding factor in determining what type of offspring a woman will produce depends directly on her overall opinion of her man and indirectly on her perceptions of herself in relation to her man. All of this occurs because these constant perceptions enable the woman to produce and transmit chemical impulses and a special genetic energy to the egg's location which ultimately produce biologically male-friendly or female-friendly environments around them. Over time, these impulses produce a kind of protective cover or homogeneous envelope around her egg that facilitates the passage of some sperm cells and not others. This situation is shown in Figure 2 where a Y-chromosome sperm-friendly environment is produced around an egg because of the woman's very favorable outlook toward her mate. The figure shows that the environmental envelope surrounding the egg has, in essence, produced a barrier to X-carrying sperm and, therefore, only the Y carriers may successfully penetrate.

Because the woman's perception of her mate is the overriding factor, it should be easy to discern that whereas a particular woman may produce five boys with one mate, it is altogether possible that that same woman would produce five girls with a different mate. The outcome would simply depend on her perceptions and opinions of the man she ended up with, and would have nothing to do with any predestined ability on her part to produce more boys than girls. It should also be clear that the converse is also true. That is, a particular man may produce three girls with one woman whose opinion of him is generally negative, but that same man may very well have produced three boys with another woman whose opinion of him was extremely positive.

A different situation may arise if tension exists among the various perceptions that a particular woman may have regarding her man. For example, a woman may have a generally unfavorable opinion of her mate, with some favorable feelings as well. In such cases it is possible for the egg's surrounding environment to be heterogenous rather than homogenous. Under such circumstances, the envelope defining the egg's environments will not be continuous and homogeneous such as the one shown in Figure 2. Rather, the environment will contain pockets of Y-friendly entry points in a generally X-friendly domain, like the one shown in Figure 3. As the figure shows, the overall environment will be such that passage of X-chromosome sperm will still be preferred, but it will be possible for Y-carrying

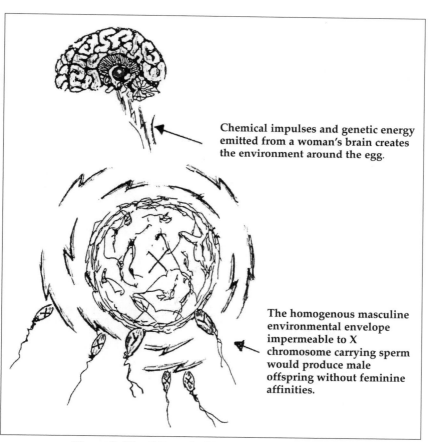

Chemical impulses and genetic energy emitted from a woman's brain creates the environment around the egg.

The homogenous masculine environmental envelope impermeable to X chromosome carrying sperm would produce male offspring without feminine affinities.

Figure 2: The Effect of a Homogenous Environment

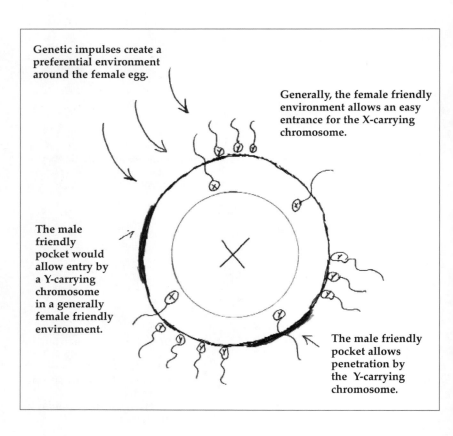

Genetic impulses create a preferential environment around the female egg.

Generally, the female friendly environment allows an easy entrance for the X-carrying chromosome.

The male friendly pocket would allow entry by a Y-carrying chromosome in a generally female friendly environment.

The male friendly pocket allows penetration by the Y-carrying chromosome.

Figure 3: The Effect of a Heterogeneous Environment

sperm to penetrate, if it encounters a Y-friendly site. The importance of such a scenario is that because the environment is predominantly female friendly, if the Y-carrying sperm is successful in penetrating the egg before the more favored X-carrying sperm, the resulting XY fetus will remain in a predominantly female friendly environment throughout the gestation period. The end product of this situation will therefore be a genetic male having female affinities. Hence, the expected result would be a sissy, a bisexual male, or a gay male, depending on how strong a female environment surrounds the egg and subsequent fetus (Figure 3).

Conversely, it should now be easy to envision that in a situation where a predominantly male friendly environment exists around the egg, but several female friendly pockets also exist, entry by an X-chromosome sperm will be affected by the predominant male environment, resulting in the opposite situation. This will ultimately produce a genetic female with masculine traits (tomboy, bisexual female, or lesbian).

Obviously, a whole spectrum of possibilities exist which determine the extent to which a particular fetus will be manipulated in an adverse environment; and it is not necessary to include a description of each individual scenario. It should be clear that the possibilities are endless, but contain definitive endpoints. At one end of the spectrum, a totally female-friendly environment produced by an unfavorable perception of a woman's mate would create a homogeneous female-friendly environment, thereby precluding penetration of Y-carrying sperm and subsequent male offspring. On the other end of the spectrum, a totally male-friendly environment created by a very favorable perception of a woman's mate would produce a homogeneous male-friendly environment, thereby precluding X-carrying sperm entry and subsequent female production. Finally, where a heterogeneous environment is produced due to a woman's ambivalent feelings towards her mate, a whole host of possibilities arise, all of which would tend to produce female or male offspring displaying differential affinities of the other sex. These various possibilities are shown in Figure 4.

It is also entirely possible for a woman's opinion of her husband to change over time. For instance, it's not hard to imagine that during the first years of marriage, a particular

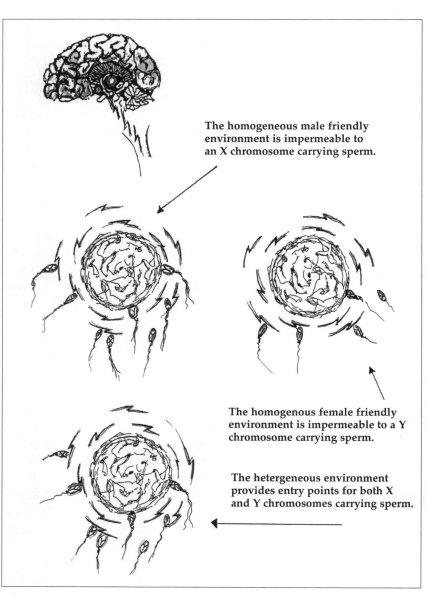

The homogeneous male friendly
environment is impermeable to
an X chromosome carrying sperm.

The homogenous female friendly
environment is impermeable to a Y
chromosome carrying sperm.

The hetergeneous environment
provides entry points for both X
and Y chromosomes carrying sperm.

Figure 4

woman may be truly in love with her husband and think the world of him, his family, his job, et cetera. Obviously at this stage of the game, the result based on the above arguments would be male offspring. However, suppose that after the first few honeymoon years, the relationship changes. Suppose the man loses his job, starts hitting the bottle, or chasing other women, which leads his wife to despise him, or worse yet, hate him. If she chooses to stay in the relationship and becomes pregnant several years later after the original positive perceptions have given way to an overall negative opinion of her mate, the result will be a new environment around the reproductive system that will preferentially facilitate entry of an X-carrying sperm chromosome, rather than a Y-carrying sperm, thereby leading to female offspring instead of a male.

The reverse is also true. It would be easy to imagine a situation where a woman initially marries a man for reasons other than true love for him. She may initially feel that she could have done better, he is not financially stable, he may be from an inferior background, et cetera. At this stage she would more than likely create an environment which would selectively filter out Y-carrying sperm cells. However, over time her husband may become successful and rich, and she may fall in love with him truly and wholeheartedly. In this situation, her brain-triggered impulses change the biological environment she produces around her reproductive tract, thereby facilitating the production of male offspring.

Hence, it is easy to envision situations where couples may have both female and male offspring. These simply track the various stages of the relationship of the individuals involved and yield specific insight into the woman's feelings toward her mate prior to the various pregnancies.

Manipulation of the Fetus in a Changing Environment

Apart from the external environment a woman creates around her reproductive cell, an additional mechanism that sometimes has drastic effects on the offspring is the environment within the womb itself, which may directly affect the growing fetus after conception has occurred. This process is related to the mechanism described above with one important difference; it has nothing to do with gender determination. Rather, this mechanism is triggered during the pregnancy itself, usually because of catastrophic events that drastically alter the woman's thought processes and, consequently, drastically alter her perception of her man relatively instantaneously.

This instantaneously created environment has nothing to do with the determination of the sex of the baby itself, but it does have everything to do with the sexual manipulation of the already existing fetus. Because this mechanism requires truly catastrophic events during the pregnancy, it is a relatively rare event which gives rise to unique offspring. Before describing the factors which catalyze this mechanism, I will briefly describe the physical aspects of how it works so that we can all envision the process while it is occurring. Then I will offer some explanations regarding how exactly this kind of relatively rare situation develops from the psychological aspects of the woman's perception-building process.

As noted earlier, once a given environment has been produced, either X- or Y-carrying sperm are preferentially filtered through to the waiting egg. Also as noted, in some instances, isolated pockets exist around the egg that may actually affect the entering sperm, but only those that are preferred, either X or Y, will be allowed in. The mechanism that we're speaking of now does not occur, if at all, until a fetus is in place within the womb. In these instances, the fetus itself is affected by the changing internal environment of the womb after gender selection is already complete. In this case severe problems may manifest themselves in the genetic offspring, and the result may very well be a homosexual, bisexual, transsexual, or in the very extreme cases, a hermaphrodite offspring or, alternatively, a mentally or physically handicapped child.

Exactly how this phenomenon works may best be described by providing a hypothetical example. Let's assume that a woman who has fallen in love with the man of her dreams becomes pregnant after the first year of marriage. As we've already seen, according to my theory, the expected child would be a baby boy. This is because all of the chemical impulses eminating from the woman's brain would create a biological environment around the egg that would selectively inhibit X-carrying sperm from entering, thereby allowing only Y-carrying sperm to successfully impregnate the egg. However, let's further assume that after conception a terrible tragedy occurs to our hypothetical couple. For example, shortly after pregnancy the woman discovers that her beloved husband has been unfaithful to her, or that he has been exposed as a criminal, or lost all of his money at a gambling hall, or any other serious mishap that suddenly changes the wife's perception of her mate. Obviously at this stage of the game, the Y chromosome has already penetrated the egg and therefore the sex of the offspring has already been determined. This does not end the matter, however. This is because just as the woman has the ability to create an external environment for her eggs, she also has the same ability to control the internal environment of her womb and fetus after fertilization, depending on what impulses "feed" the fetus.

This process can easily be understood by realizing that once a particular environment has been created by the woman's thought processes and feelings toward her mate, the environment is capable of affecting individual eggs as well as a newly growing fetus. This is because the environmental envelope surrounds both the unfertilized egg and subsequent fetus, should fertilization occur. In the general case, an environment will not change drastically during the 9-month gestation period and, therefore, drastic changes during this stage will not take place. For example, assuming that the environment surrounding the egg is strongly masculine, and feelings remain relatively the same during the gestation period, the fetus will simply be strengthened by the pre-existing environment. Similarly, if a strongly feminine environment remains intact, a strong feminine fetus will develop in that same environment. Furthermore, if the pre-existing environment around the egg contains small pockets which prefer Y-carrying sperm and relatively large pockets predisposed to X-carrying sperm, but a Y chromosome still manages to penetrate, the overwhelming feminine nature of the egg's envelope will predispose the subsequent fetus, although biologically male, to bisexuality, transsexuality or homosexuality. The process is the same in reverse for the female fetus.

However, the possibility also exists that what was once a strongly masculine environment all the way until conception may be severely affected by a drastic change in circumstances after conception. When catastrophic changes do occur during the pregnancy itself, drastic changes in the woman's feelings toward her husband will eminate from her brain and create a new and distinct biological environment not only outside the fetus's location but inside the womb as well, as shown in Figure 5.

These new impulses will attempt to transform what was initially a Y-friendly internal environment to a new Y-hostile environment. Genetically, of course, this will be next to impossible to achieve because once fertilized, the XY fetus cannot be spontaneously changed to an XX fetus (or so the scientific community tells us, although I have my doubts). Instead, what will most likely occur is that the XY fetus will be manipulated to take on more and more XX characteristics as the pregnancy continues, yet will still retain its XY genetic signature. The net result of this, of course, will be a biological male with feminine affinities, or in other words, a bisexual, homosexual, or even a transexual male. Therefore, just as the sexual orientation of any given offspring may be affected by the environment in place before conception, the same result may be obtained by manipulation and drastic changes within the environment after conception during the gestation period.

Depending on the frequency and intensity of the new chemical impulses produced by the different thought processes the woman is experiencing, the results may be more drastic. For example, a genetic male embryo or fetus may, in fact, be manipulated in such a way that it becomes a genetic man trapped in the mind of a woman (i.e. a transsexual) later in life. And in very rare instances, the manipulation may be so intense that a true hermaphrodite results, in which case the offspring will contain both male and female genitalia. Yet the resulting person will mentally identify him- or herself exclusively with one sex or the other.

This may sound incredible and even absurd to some, but I submit that there is at least some evidence to support this theory. It is indisputable that all of the available research suggests that both male-to-female and female-to-male transsexuals have one thing in common. They all seem to have identified with the opposite sex (i.e., their genetic opposite) ever since they were born, or at least as far back as they themselves can remember. Moreover, although controversial, the available research also seems to indicate that homosexuality is an inherited rather than

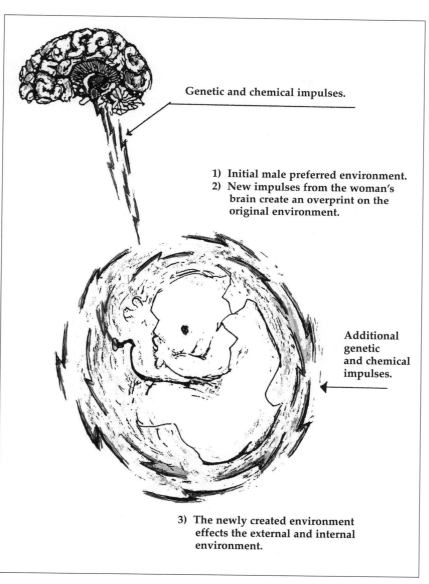

Genetic and chemical impulses.

1) Initial male preferred environment.
2) New impulses from the woman's brain create an overprint on the original environment.

Additional genetic and chemical impulses.

3) The newly created environment effects the external and internal environment.

Figure 5: Catastrophic Changes During Pregnancy

an environmentally-induced phenomenon. Clearly, if this is actually the case, as it seems to be, then it must logically follow that the woman rather than the man is responsible for these phenomena. After all, the man merely provides a seed, and is only involved in the whole process of childbearing for a split second! While it is true that man's sperm does carry a genetic code, to my knowledge there are no studies that have demonstrated that predisposition to homosexuality or transsexuality is either inherited or transmitted in such a way. The most logical and consistent explanation must be that such phenomena occur through the direct manipulation of the womb and fetus by the woman's thought processes, which stimulate chemical impulses that effect the womb directly and, consequently, the growing fetus.

Obviously, the hermaphrodite situation is much more difficult to explain. It may very well be that such creatures are really the result of a genetic oddity. However, some studies have shown that such persons often have XXY or XYY chromosomal signatures, suggesting that some direct manipulation or chromosomal overprint has occurred. If the intensity and frequency of chemical impulses are extreme, then it should be relatively easy to envision that the overprint, if one in fact occurs, is due to a continuous supply of feminine or masculine impulses arising after the initial normal XY or XX fetus has already been produced. It also naturally follows that because such situations require such extreme genetic manipulation, this type of phenomena would rarely occur, as exemplified by the very rare numbers of true hermaphrodites. As a result, in terms of the sheer number of cases, homosexuals (either male or female), which require moderate fetal manipulation, should be most common, followed by transsexuals (either male-to-female or female-to-male), which require more intense manipulation. Finally true hermaphrodites would be the rarest of all since they require very extreme manipulation. And this is exactly what is observed in the general population. Homosexuals are far and away the largest group, followed by transsexuals, a distant second, and hermaphrodites, which are extremely rare.

When viewed from this perspective, it becomes increasingly clear that "normal" males and females are simply the product of the right type of sperm fertilizing the "right" type of environment, or the synchronization of gender and sexual orientation. On the other hand, a woman or a man having an "abnormal" sexual orientation simply reflects the wrong type of sperm fertilizing the "wrong" type of environment. In other words, if a Y-carrying sperm is successful in penetrating a predominantly female friendly environment, the result will be nonsynchronization (to various degrees, as we've already seen) of gender and sexual orientation and, consequently, a sexually confused or sexually "abnormal" adult.

One additional possibility that may occur by this method, that is, manipulation of the fetus after conception, is a physical or mental handicap in the offspring. Most likely this situation does not involve the woman's thought processes regarding her mate during pregnancy, but may involve abnormal thought processes regarding other matters. As I explained in the earlier chapters, I am aware of children born with certain physical defects that may have been triggered by a particular desire that their mother was deprived of during pregnancy. Remember the little girl born with the coffee stain on her face? How about the policeman's son that resembled a monkey more than a human being at birth? In both these cases, family members of the person in question remembered a triggering moment during the mother's pregnancy that they believed may have ultimately been responsible for the child's physical defects.

Although I am not as convinced that these situations are directly related to the mother's deprived desires during pregnancy, it certainly does not take a rocket scientist to conclude that such oddities may very well result from the mother's odd and abnormal thought processes during gestation, which affect the womb and growing fetus in strange and particular ways. After all, if thought processes inspired by music that a mother listens to can be linked to the creation of certain "maternal genes" capable of instilling certain superior musical traits in newborns, as Dr. Hammer of the National Institutes of Health has suggested, then it stands to reason that other inexplicable physical and psychological traits observed in newborns may be attributed to similar thought processes as well.

I realize that many may think that this is a really far-fetched hypothesis. Before you dismiss it outright, however, I suggest that you first think about it very carefully and then conduct your own empirical study by way of observation and some research. First, examine your immediate family, then perhaps your family circle, then your friends and acquaintances. Try to begin with people that you know pretty well, those whose relationships you're familiar with, and examine their offspring. I predict that you will be shocked at the results you find as you make your way through more and more people. Then, out of curiosity, look at some of the research done in this area. You don't have to go to the high-powered medical journals, you can start with simple overviews in magazines and newspapers; and then perhaps you can look at the more sophisticated stuff. I'm confident that you will begin to agree with me as you delve deeper and deeper into the subject matter.

For starters you may want to step back and take a look at your own family and think about the unique relationship that your parents had. Would such a relationship be more conducive to the production of males or females according to my theory? If you come from a family of five boys, I'm sure you'll find that your mother truly loved your father in every way and that she generally looked up to him and trusted him wholeheartedly. You'll probably also realize that, at least with respect to your immediate family, there is no question that it was your father who was in control of every aspect of the relationship and the family, probably in a stern but fair way, and, most importantly, when you're finally done analyzing the situation, you'll realize that your mother respected that and wanted it that way.

If, on the other hand, you come from a family of five girls, I trust that you'll find exactly the opposite. Perhaps your mother was always in control of your father, or perhaps she was the rich one in the family, or the more educated one. Maybe you'll discover that she came from a very wealthy background compared to that of your father's. Alternatively, you may discover that your mother was a very beautiful, active, and self-assured woman, while your father was a relatively ugly, passive man having a relatively low self-esteem. As you search deeper and deeper, you'll come to see that my theory will be accurate every single time.

If you're still not satisfied after you've examined your family and those of your close friends, you may want to look at the latest research that's been done on the subject. If you do, you'll find that more and more frequently, researchers are discovering that mothers have much more to do with the characteristics of their offspring than was previously thought. You'll also discover that a distinct difference exists among X-carrying sperm and Y-carrying sperm, and that it is now easy to synthetically differentiate the two into separate populations by chemical methods. Certainly the next logical step will occur to you as it did to me. If it is so easy to differentiate the two synthetically, imagine how easy it must be to differentiate between the two types of sperm naturally, in the mother's reproductive tract?

Then if you still have doubts, you may want to go out and speak to some transsexual and homosexual people. They won't bite, at least not the ones without a chip on their shoulder about their orientation or those trying to make a political statement. Ask them whether or not they have always felt the way they do about their orientation. Better yet, ask them if they've ever discussed the issue of when they were born with their mother, father, or grandparents. Ask them all of this before you tell them about the premise of this book, not after. If you do it that way, you'll be surprised to find that, indeed, they have felt the way they now do for their whole life, and those who have discussed the situation with their mothers and fathers invariably will tell you what I've already related to you. They will tell you that something catastrophic did in fact occur while their mother was carrying them to term, although most will say that they never attributed those events as anything to do with their orientation.

Of course, I cannot make a believer out of a predestined nonbeliever, so you must approach the subject with an open mind; otherwise you'll concentrate on the possible rare exceptions (although I have not been able to find any in the thousands of case studies that I have personally analyzed) rather than the general conclusion. But in an effort to show you what I mean, let's briefly take a took at two recognizable case studies.

Well-known Case Studies

With respect to the theory that I have presented, there are two well known "classified" cases: the late Princess Diana and her sister-in-law, Sarah Ferguson, the Duchess of York. They represent two contrasting and well documented case studies in an otherwise long laundry list of examples.

With respect to Princess Diana, it is undisputed that from the very outset of her relationship with Prince Charles, she was absolutely in love with him. In fact, many of the early news releases that carefully followed their relationship, which are too numerous to even tally, consistently described her as "adoring" her prince. The union, from her perspective, was described as a "fairy tale too good to be true." In all of the photographs taken of the couple in the early years before the relationship turned sour, Prince Charles looked like an honest-to-God prince charming, and Diana would always appear gazing at him in adoration.

To test the theory, we cannot look at the relationship in hindsight. Rather, we must look at it while it was occurring. We need to reflect on Diana's opinion of her charming prince in the early years when she bore him children. During that time her love for him was so immense and she so admired him that it is no wonder that she produced two wonderful baby boys for him. As we've already seen, this was the simple result of chemical impulses that she was emitting (albeit unbeknownst to her) from her brain directly to her reproductive system, which created a very strong and intense male-preferred environment directly related to her perceptions of her wonderful prince.

On the other side of the coin we have Sarah Ferguson, the sister-in-law. Clearly a very feisty woman, Fergie (as she's been referred to) had a completely different opinion of her prince. To her, Andrew was simply a toy. She knew from the outset that Andrew adored her in every way, and that she could do what she wanted with him. As such, she was aware from the very beginning that she was in total control of the relationship. In fact, in some of the news releases concerning a book that she intended to write, she disclosed how she disliked Andrew in bed and his boring sexual behavior. In addition, she was proud of the fact that although Diana "liked to be dominated in bed," she, Sarah, preferred to take the initiative. In addition, as if this weren't enough, she got to the point of carrying on an affair with her lover right under the prince's nose and was actually caught in *flagrante delicto* on one occasion when the prince walked in on her and her lover.

Unlike Diana, Sarah Ferguson produced two little girls for Prince Andrew. This should come as no surprise to anyone. In fact, knowing what I knew, I had predicted it all along. In this case, Sarah's perception of superiority relative to her mate, regardless of whether true or not, allowed her to create a preferential female environment which subsequently led to the birth of the two girls. It is not necessary for me to go into all of the supporting evidence for this. The relationships described above are well documented and available to all who are interested, and they remain the classic examples supporting my theory.

Of course, I could go on and on, providing numerous examples of similar situations where the theory has proved to be infallible. But rather than recount the many examples, I'll leave that up to the reader. Instead, what I want to look at next are the consequences that such a theory inevitably leads to. They are quite serious indeed. To do them justice would require a separate book much lengthier than the present one. However, in the next chapter, I'll briefly outline some of the natural consequences that necessarily flow from this hypothesis, and point out why the consequences are so dire indeed, and why, at least at the present time, I see no remedy on the horizon.

5

FEMINISM AND THE PRODUCTS OF THE FUTURE

Anytime someone spends forty-plus years pondering a certain theory such as I have, they can't help but think about the philosophical implications that must naturally follow if such a theory holds true. Assuming for the moment that I am correct, and that women do actually determine the gender of their children, then the current feminist movement in the industrialized world may actually change civilization as we know it, and here's why.

As we all know, in the last thirty years or so, women have made significant strides in society. The majority of women now work. They earn wages, which in many cases are comparable to those of men. They occupy positions which traditionally have been reserved for men. And they have also become a political force to be reckoned with. It is not unusual these days to find that women are waiting until their thirties to even consider marriage, and by that time they've already established a career for themselves. And they no longer are restricted to secretarial or clerical positions either, as they once were. These days we have women firefighters, police officers, professional basketball players, and even wrestlers.

In short, the in-vogue thing for women to do these days is to be equal to men, not only in terms of the wages they earn, but in all aspects of life. Women want to compete with men on all levels. Some of the more radical feminists even go so far as being men bashers and men haters, blaming all of the problems faced by women on men. This is generally seen as a good thing, not because it really is, but because it is the politically correct thing to do. Politicians in power do not want to come out publicly and say that the feminist movement is a socially counterproductive one, because if they do, they would have to face the music on election day and most likely would be booted out of office, given the large number of women voters.

The fact is that this feminist movement has created certain heretofore unimaginable and unforeseen consequences. First, because women have now established themselves in the work force, they can no longer assume the motherly role that they did several decades ago. The traditional family has deteriorated to daycare centers instead of motherly love, TV dinners instead of home-cooked meals, and kids hanging out on street comers with wannabe gangbangers, instead of sitting at home with their families waiting for dad to get home from work.

The greatest consequence, however, has been the change in women's philosophical outlook on their role in life in general, and their opinion towards men in particular. They now consider themselves equal to men in many, if not all, ways; and they no longer see themselves as needing men for anything in life, not even for reproductive purposes. After all, these days women can become impregnated by simply going to a sperm bank and obtaining in vitro fertilization. Moreover, daycare can take care of their synthetically-produced child while they pursue their careers, so that they can pay for the daycare and show everyone that they are just as capable as men in making their way through the world. Obviously, not all women have this kind of mindset, but the proportion of women pursuing this lifestyle is steadily increasing. Which brings me to the most significant consequence society now faces.

Because women have made these changes, their feelings towards men in particular have changed. They no longer see men as they once did. Now that they have equaled them in the work force and are approaching them in political stature, more and more frequently, women are looking at men as commodities, not necessities. They can survive just as well without them as they can with them. Certainly these changing perceptions have a direct impact on the chemical impulses their brain produces and sends down to their reproductive system. If my theory is correct, it has a direct and tragic result on the offspring that such women will ultimately produce.

Let's examine a typical modem relationship between a man and a woman of the nineties. First of all, they probably both work and plan on doing so both before and after the marriage They're both perfectly capable of providing for themselves, and to that extent they are financially independent. Because of their financial independence, in some cases prenuptial agreements will be arranged so that if anyone decides to get out of the marriage, they will both retain their financial independence. Also, because of their combined income, having children will not cause problems because daycare centers or nannies will be available to take care of them. Moreover, because the woman has an income, she knows that whether or not the relationship works out is not a really big deal, because the man is fungible anyway, and she'll always be able to find someone else if he doesn't work out. In the end, the marriage will probably end up in divorce, because the two people probably got married for convenience and financial reasons, not true love and devotion. Once the divorce is final, the two people will eventually meet other mates and the cycle will repeat itself, except that by this time, the woman might be too old to bear more children. Now I know that not all of the marriages occurring these days are like the one I've just outlined, but what I am saying is that such a scenario is becoming more and more commonplace.

For the purposes of this discussion, the key lies in trying to perceive what women such as the ones in the above example must be thinking when they enter into a relationship with a man. In doing so, it is important to keep in mind those factors discussed in Chapter 4 that help determine what the likely gender production of such women would be. A brief review of the list would suggest the following results. Certainly the woman in the above hypothetical example will not perceive her husband as intellectually superior to herself. After all, she's probably had just as much schooling as he has; and as far as careers go, she's just as successful as he is. She's probably also likely to feel generally superior and better than others because of what she's been able to achieve on her own in life. She's likely to be ambitious as well since her foremost concerns will be her career, financial position, and social status. Consequently, she will probably also feel that her husband, as well as the rest of humanity, owes her something, because she's not only managed to get married and have children but she's also a very successful businesswoman or lawyer or doctor on top of it. She's likely to think that compared to her, her husband probably doesn't rate because he's had it much easier than she has. After all, she had to worry about a career and kids, while he's just had to worry about the career. Certainly her mate's money won't mean much to her, because she can easily take care of that department without him; and if he doesn't watch it and do exactly as she wishes, she just might. This does not mean that she won't like anything about her husband (if she's even bothered to marry). Certainly there will be aspects of his physique, personality, or intellect that she'll be fond of; otherwise, she would have picked someone else to be with. But let's face it, at best she will have ambivalent feelings about him, with respect to most things that are important to her in life.

Undoubtedly, this type of mindset on her part will lead to the production of chemical impulses, or genetic energy, which will not produce a homogeneous male-preferred environment. Rather, what will be produced, even in the best case scenario, is a heterogeneous environment around her reproductive system, which will be generally preferential to female production but will contain some possible Y-sperm entry points. Of course, if this is the case, then the expected result will be a boy having feminine traits. Furthermore, the intensity of those feminine traits will depend on the nature and extent of the heterogeneous environment. In addition, if any major disruptions occur after conception but before birth, then the situation is likely to get worse; and the developing fetus will be affected to an even greater degree, possibly leading to a bisexual male, a homosexual male, transsexual, et cetera.

Given that the numbers of these so-called liberated women are increasing (and, despite reports of a backlash, there is no doubt that the numbers are increasing), the situation is likely to not only continue but get much worse. Hence, when looked at in this fashion, it is no wonder that the number of bisexuals, homosexuals, and transsexuals is on the increase. Those increasing numbers simply reflect a growing number of women who see themselves as being equal, superior to, or rebellious towards men; the resulting reproductive environment that they create, and the biological consequences thereof. It is unlikely that the situation will change either. This is because women will not be willing to give up the "progress" that they have made over the past few decades. Going back to a woman's designated role in the 1950s is akin to death to a woman of the nineties. Moreover, given women's newfound political clout, legislative reform on women's and family issues is likely to be counterproductive because any anticipated changes are likely to favor and perpetuate, rather than hinder and stop, the movement.

So what lies ahead? The family unit as we know it, although not completely obsolete, has undergone such profound changes in the last few years that it is no longer clear to anyone what a "family" is. The gay and lesbian subcultures would have you believe that a child with two mothers or two fathers is just as much part of a legitimate family as a child with a mother and a father. Perhaps this is so to some feminist professor sitting at his or her desk behind ivory towers, but this is certainly not the case to most other people, and most of all not to me.

The young people of today are confused about their roles in a sexual context, because an innocent compliment may result in a sexual harassment lawsuit, or even worse, criminal charges. Indeed, all a woman has to do these days is simply utter the very words, and a man's livelihood or his very life may be destroyed forever. Women know this and take advantage of it. Furthermore, it does not matter whether the man is president, supreme court justice, athlete, or successful businessman. From Monica Lewinsky to Anita Hill to Desiree Washington to countless others, women have now concluded that a simple accusation, whether true or not, will bring any man to his knees and, at the same time, will bring the woman fame and fortune by way of book deals, lecture circuits, and Hollywood productions. Moreover, they also know that they'll likely be regarded as the hopeless victims while the men will be perceived as sexually disturbed individuals or uncontrollable lechers. Again, not because that's the truth, but simply because any other reaction will mean political suicide. In essence, men have become pawns in a game of chess where women, realizing the power they have, are now rewriting the rules of the game.

The men that are currently in power are either unable or unwilling to do anything about it, mainly because of the possible political repercussions. From Senator Packwood to Governor

Lowry to President Clinton, the message has been heard loud and clear. In fact, the message has been so loud that many men are now calling themselves feminists, not because they really are, but because it is the politically correct thing to do. To not do so may imply that they disagree with the feminist movement itself, and this of course would have political consequences. Politics aside, some men jump on the feminism bandwagon because they are romantically involved with a feminist, who may be very shapely indeed; and, of course, if he doesn't pretend to also be a feminist, there will be sexual consequences for him. He may find himself sleeping on the couch indefinitely, or better yet, out of the house and out on the street, with only monthly child support bills to look forward to.

As for the women, to their credit, they've figured it out. They alone are the ones responsible for creating new life, and knowing that this is the ultimate desire of any man, they have realized that they are in control of the species and certainly that they are the superior sex. The problem is, they don't know what I stumbled on forty years ago and have related to you in the preceding pages. Because of this, they are misplacing their superiority and channeling it toward being equal or superior to men in those aspects of life which are counterproductive, if the human species and family circle as we know them are to survive. This is because they no longer see men as protectors and providers, husbands and fathers, necessary to raise a family. Instead, they see them as sperm donors and business colleagues, roommates and lovers, simply convenient for the selfish gratification of their libidos, sharing of household chores, and viable escorts for special occasions.

As a result of all this, the resultant reproductive system in many of today's women, particularly in the industrialized world, is being shaped by a genetic energy that favors a heterogeneous environment with its many consequences. The trouble with this is that the lives that are being produced are sexually confused and handicapped from the beginning, which not only amplifies but also perpetuates the problem for the future.

If there is a silver lining in this otherwise bleak prediction, it is those couples who marry for all the right reasons. The ones that love and admire each other equally. The husbands and fathers who love their wife above all else, and work hard for the well being of their family and the financial stability of their loved ones. The wives and mothers who look forward to raising their children, protecting them, and above all, teaching them how to be decent human beings. Those that are happy to see their husbands come home from work as they feed their children for the umpteenth time. Such women produce healthy environments, not only inside but outside of their bodies as well. They are the desire of any man, and it's tragic indeed that their numbers are dwindling.